FYNBOS

JOHN MANNING

PHOTOGRAPHS BY JOHN MANNING
AND COLIN PATERSON-JONES

Published by Struik Nature
(an imprint of Penguin Random House South Africa (Pty) Ltd)
Reg. No. 1953/000441/07
The Estuaries No. 4, Oxbow Crescent,
Century Avenue, Century City, 7441
PO Box 1144, Cape Town, 8000 South Africa

First published in 2020
10 9 8 7 6 5 4 3 2 1

Publisher: Pippa Parker
Managing editor: Roelien Theron
Editor: Natalie Bell
Designer: Gillian Black
Proofreader: Thea Grobbelaar

ISBN 978 1 77584 695 6 (Print)
ISBN 978 1 77584 694 9 (ePub)

Reproduction by Studio Repro and Hirt & Carter Cape (Pty) Ltd
Printed and bound in China by 1010 Printing International Ltd.

Front cover: *Phaenocoma prolifera*
Title page: *Protea mucronifolia*, a rare protea only
found north of Wellington, Western Cape

Acknowledgements

This Pocket Guide is extracted and amplified
from the highly popular *Field Guide to Fynbos*.
As in that publication and in many others of
mine, I am indebted to Elizabeth Parker and the
Mapula Trust for their ongoing commitment to
conservation and education.

CONTENTS

Plant groups

The species in this book have been divided into 10 groups based on the form of the plants and/or the shape of their flowers. To find the group for your plant, start with Group 1 and move through the other groups progressively. Species that fall in one group are automatically excluded from subsequent groups.

Group 1	**Grass-like plants** with minute brown flowers
Group 2	**Bulbs and orchids** with parallel leaf venation and 6 petals
Group 3	**Aloe-like plants** with succulent, mostly prickly leaves and tubular, reddish flowers with 6 petals
Group 4	**Succulents** with unarmed (not prickly) leaves and 4, 5 or an indefinite number of petals
Group 5	**Climbers** with twining stems
Group 6	Plants with **pea-like flowers**
Group 7	**Daisies, proteas and clustered flowers** in tight, button-like or fringed heads
Group 8	**Heath-like shrubs** with small, hard, mostly needle-like leaves with margins often rolled under, and regular flowers
Group 9	**Broad-leaved shrubs** with broader or softer leaves and either regular or 2-lipped flowers
Group 10	**Herbaceous plants** with non-woody stems

INTRODUCTION

Fynbos is virtually synonymous with the flora at the the southern tip of Africa.
This crescent of vegetation was long famous among botanists as the smallest
of six floral kingdoms of the world, but is now considered to be an integral, albeit
distinctive, part of the Old World Tropical Floral Kingdom. Whatever its rank, it is
home to one of the world's richest floras. Crowded within an area of a little under
91,000km^2 are some 9,250 species of flowering plants, two-thirds of which are
found nowhere else on Earth. It is small wonder that Conservation International has
identified the Cape Floristic Region as one of the 52 biodiversity hotspots on Earth.

The first evidence of the extraordinary flora of the Cape reached Europe in
the form of a dried flower head of *Protea neriifolia*, collected from the shores
of False Bay by the crew of a passing East Indiaman. It was soon followed by
bulbs of several species of amaryllis, hyacinth and iris. The flowering of these
plants in Holland in the first years of the seventeenth century ignited a passion
for fynbos flowers that has shown no sign of abating.

The term 'fynbos' (from the Dutch, *fynbosch*) was originally applied by the
settlers at the Cape to any sort of small woodland growth that did not include the
timber trees that were essential to their survival. It was only in the latter half of the
twentieth century that it gained international currency as the appropriate name for
the distinctive heathland vegetation
of the southwestern Cape.

Fynbos is the dominant natural
vegetation of the southwestern
part of South Africa, occurring
mainly on the rocky sandstone
and quartzite formations of
the Cape Fold Mountains, but
also on exposures of sand and
limestone along the coastal
shelves. On the West Coast,
these coastal sands and their
associated communities of sand
plain fynbos extend northwards
almost to the Namibian border.
Along the southern Cape coast,
outcrops of quartzitic rock allow
grassy fynbos to thrive as far east
as Grahamstown. Beyond this,
outlying fynbos communities occur
on sandstone outcrops in southern
KwaZulu-Natal near Port St Johns
and scattered along the edge
of the Drakensberg Mountains
and eastern Escarpment as far
north as Zimbabwe. Although the
fynbos communities of the eastern
seaboard are structurally similar to
Cape fynbos, they are sufficiently
distinct to be classified separately.
In this book we concern ourselves
only with Cape fynbos.

Haemanthus coccineus, growing here at Cape
Point, was in cultivation in Europe by 1603.

Major vegetation types of the southwestern Cape

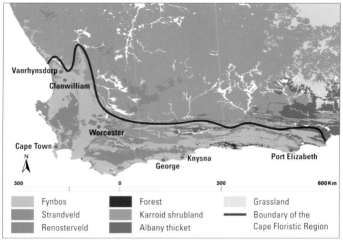

Fynbos	Forest	Grassland
Strandveld	Karroid shrubland	Boundary of the
Renosterveld	Albany thicket	Cape Floristic Region

Vanrhynsdorp
Clanwilliam
Worcester
Cape Town
N
Knysna
George
Port Elizabeth

300 0 300 600 Km

Defining fynbos

Fynbos is an evergreen, hard-leaved shrubland occurring on nutrient-poor soils, especially those derived from heavily leached sandstones or alkaline limestones. It is dominated by small- and leathery-leaved shrubs, in association with evergreen, grass-like perennials. True Cape fynbos is distinguished from other fynbos communities by the presence of Cape reeds or restios. It is unique among vegetation types in the high numbers of heaths, proteas, restios, buchus and wild irises. Fynbos is also distinguished by the presence of four endemic plant families, i.e. all of their species grow only in fynbos.

Fynbos is dominated by evergreen, small-leaved shrubs.

Many fynbos bulbs are stimulated to flower after fire.

Fynbos occurs mostly on acidic (pH4.4 or less), coarse-grained soils lacking especially in available nitrogen and phosphorus. It rarely develops where the annual rainfall is less than 400mm per annum or where droughts are common. It also grows on the porous, infertile soils on limestones.

True fynbos vegetation is analogous to the heathlands of other regions with a Mediterranean climate. It excludes renosterveld, another evergreen, fine-leaved vegetation type of the southwestern Cape. Fynbos shrubs vary greatly in height and density but are mostly richly branched with twisted boles – true trees are virtually absent.

The understorey always contains a conspicuous admixture of Cape reeds or restios, which may become dominant in some communities. Grasses are uncommon in most fynbos communities. Bulbous plants are normally plentiful but are generally evident only in the year or two after wildfires clear the vegetation. Most stands of fynbos contain many species, in some cases up to 120 different kinds in a single 100m² quadrat, and it is rare that a single species dominates a community, except locally.

Within Cape fynbos, botanists recognise several different plant communities, distinguished by their dominant elements. The occurrence of these communities is determined primarily by the amount of available moisture, relative proportion of summer rainfall, intensity of summer drought and fertility of the soil.

Fynbos diversity

Cape fynbos plant communities naturally cover over 41,000km², or a little under half the area of the Cape Floristic Region, but are estimated to include 70–80 per cent of the species, making Cape fynbos the most diverse vegetation type in the region. According to some measures, it may in fact be two or three times as diverse as the rainforests of the New and Old World tropics. The secret to this extraordinary diversity lies in the scale at which it is measured.

At a more local level, tropical rainforests are easily the most diverse habitats on Earth; the key to fynbos diversity is the rapid change in individual species among sites within the vegetation as a whole. Put in another way, Cape fynbos has an exceptionally high proportion of highly localised species, some of them restricted to a single locality of less than 1km². This is in sharp contrast to tropical forests, in which individual species are typically widely scattered, and is one of the reasons it is so difficult to identify fynbos species: each locality is likely to have a large number of different or unique species.

Fire and fynbos

Evidence suggests that in the absence of regular fires, all but the drier fynbos types would become dominated by trees. Fynbos can thus be considered to be a fire-dependent vegetation type, along with grasslands and savannas.

The infertility of fynbos soils means that the recycling of soil nutrients is essential for fynbos survival. Fire is the motor that drives this cycle. Fires at appropriate intervals are not only an integral but an essential part of fynbos ecology. They rejuvenate the vegetation by recycling precious nutrients back into the soil. They also remove the choking canopy that has grown up during the intervening years, allowing light to reach the soil surface.

Fynbos shrubs that have been burned take several years to recover, either through seeds or regrowth. In the meantime, the space that has been opened promotes the

Periodic fires clear moribund vegetation and enrich the soil.

growth of herbaceous plants. These plants take advantage of the flush of newly released nutrients and favourable growing conditions to complete short life cycles, returning to the soil as seeds once larger shrubs overwhelm them. Here they lie dormant until the next fire triggers their germination.

Fires in fynbos occur optimally every 10–14 years. Whereas bulbs and fire ephemerals flourish with more frequent burns, many shrubs only reach reproductive maturity after several years. Too frequent fires, usually the result of human intervention, destroy the adult plants of such species and exhaust their seed banks, bringing about their local extinction.

Fynbos flowers

Flowering in fynbos is concentrated in spring. Between half and two-thirds of the species are in flower during this short period, although at least a fifth may be found in bloom throughout the year. Several fynbos bulbs, including most amaryllis species, have separated their growing and flowering phases, enabling them to flower in the dry season, in midsummer or autumn.

Many fynbos flowers are often strikingly beautiful. This reflects the wide variety of strategies for attracting pollinators, many of which are uncommon elsewhere. Over 400 fynbos species are adapted to pollination by birds, for instance. This is proportionally about twice as many as in southern Africa as a whole. Sunbirds and sugarbirds pollinate some of the most iconic fynbos plants, including the more showy

Southern Double-collared Sunbird pollinating *Kniphofia uvaria* (Aloe family).

Mountain pride butterfly, *Meneris tulbaghia*, pollinates scarlet-flowered fynbos species.

heaths, proteas and pincushions. Several other spectacular, scarlet-flowered fynbos species, including the Red disa, rely on the summer-flying Mountain pride butterfly for their pollination. Other specialised fynbos pollinators include rodents, nectar-feeding horseflies and tangle-veined flies, and furry-bodied monkey beetles. Each of these groups has driven the evolution of distinct classes of flowers that contribute to the beauty of Cape fynbos.

Fynbos conservation

The diversity of fynbos dramatically increases the danger of extinction for a substantial proportion of its unique plants. Nearly one in three plant species in the Cape Floristic Region is classified as Rare or Endangered. This amounts to more than 2,000 fynbos species and the number continues to rise. The greatest threat to these plants is habitat loss. Another major threat is the encroachment of alien vegetation. Fires at too frequent intervals threaten the local survival of certain species that are unable to re-establish under such a regime. Still others are at risk from the collection of wild plants for traditional medicinal use. The responsibility for conservation rests with the individual, and everyone can make a difference. Join local interest groups concerned with conservation in your neighbourhood, or adopt a small site with threatened species on it. With so many species living precariously on tiny fragments, fynbos needs all the help it can get to survive.

How to use this book

1. Group number and name for identification. The grouping is the main organising principle of this Pocket Guide. Turn to the Contents page for further information.

2. Genus botanical name

3. Species botanical name

4. Common/vernacular names in English and Afrikaans

5. Species distribution map

6. Species description. Numbers in parentheses are exceptional (out of the norm but occasionally encountered)

7. Paragraph of interest

8. Flowering months

9. Floral key

How to read the floral key

The floral key is a valuable addition to identification. It is a simple shorthand code for the number and position of the 4 main floral organs:

sepals petals stamens ovaries

S3 P3 St3 <u>O</u>

This flower has 3 sepals, 3 petals, 3 stamens and a superior ovary.

- Numerals represent the numbers of each organ in a single flower.
- ~ indicates an indefinite number.
- Male ♂ and female ♀ symbols are used for male and female flowers.
- <u>O</u> represents a superior ovary; O represents an inferior ovary.

stamen (St)
petal (P)
sepal (S)

Do not be fooled!

Readers should note that the 'flowers' of daisies and proteas are actually clusters of many individual small flowers. In many daisies, the outer florets in the head are developed into strap-like structures that mimic the true petals of more conventional flowers.

Ovaries

superior ovary (<u>O</u>)
(above sepals and petals)

inferior ovary (O)
(below sepals and petals)

In very rare instances, the sepals and petals arise midway up the ovary, which is then termed half-inferior (indicated in the floral key as Ø).

Examples

♂S3 St12 ♀S3 O

Male flower: 3 sepals, 0 petals and 12 stamens. **Female flower:** 3 sepals, 0 petals and an inferior ovary.

S5 P~ St~ O

This flower has 5 sepals, an indefinite number of petals, an indefinite number of stamens and an inferior ovary.

Floral keys are not given for the grass-like species (pages 10–11) as their flowers are too small to be studied without a microscope.

Sep–Feb

Prionium serratum
Palmrush, Palmiet

Robust, rush-like, aquatic shrub to 2m, with fibrous stems bearing terminal rosettes of hard, grey, strap-like leaves with sharply saw-toothed margins. Flowers in large, branched clusters on 3-angled stem, small and star-shaped, brown, with 6 dry petals, 6 stamens, and a superior ovary with 3 long style branches. **HABITAT:** River banks and in or near streams on sandstone, often forming dense stands, in the Western and Eastern Cape, and southern KwaZulu-Natal.

There is a single species in Africa, with a few relatives in wet habitats in South America. The leaves were used to make conical hats called *toedangs* that were worn by Malay slaves in early Cape Town. Palmiet wetlands are critical ecosystem regulators, maintaining hydrological stability and water quality.

♀   ♂

Mar–Apr

Thamnochortus insignis
Albertinia thatching reed, Dekriet

Large, tufted perennial with jointed, unbranched stems to 2m. Sexes are on separate plants: male florets in many nodding, tassel-like spikelets, and female florets in stiffly erect spikelets 15–25mm long, each with a solitary style. Fruits are small, soft-walled nutlets enclosed within winged bracts. **HABITAT:** Loamy soils between coastal dunes on the Agulhas Plain.

Dekriet was the main species used for thatched roofs of Cape Dutch homes in the southern Cape, and is cultivated commercially for this. Plants have become established along roadsides well beyond their original range on the Agulhas Plain, from seeds that have fallen from the reeds during transportation after harvesting. The architectural form and coppery flowers make it an attractive garden ornamental.

Elegia capensis
Horsetail reed, Fonteinriet

 Robust, brush-like perennial to 2m, with stiffly erect stems bearing attractive papery sheaths at the joints, from which arise dense whorls of sterile branchlets. The sexes are on separate plants, in aggregations of spikelets, the female florets each with 3 styles. The fruits are small nutlets enclosed within winged bracts. **HABITAT**: Seeps and streamsides on sandstone slopes in the Western and Eastern Cape.

Fonteinriet is a popular pondside ornamental in temperate gardens, locally and elsewhere. The stems were traditionally bound to staffs for use as brooms.

Nov–Mar

Ficinia radiata
Chrome stargrass, Stergras

 Tufted perennial, 5–25cm, with a cluster of narrow, sharply keeled leaves at the base of the 3-angled stem. The bright yellow spikelets are borne in heads at the tip of the stem, surrounded by radiating, leafy, chrome-yellow bracts. **HABITAT**: Sandy flats and lower slopes in moist places in the southwestern Cape, often conspicuous after fire.

The brightest member in a genus of more than 60 species, Chrome stargrass can be common on sandy flats in the spring following a wildfire. As in most sedges, the 3-angled flowering stem distinguishes it from grasses and reeds, which have cylindrical stems.

Sep–Nov

S1 St8–16 <u>O</u>   Jul–Dec

Aponogeton distachyos
Pondblossom, Waterblommetjie

 Rhizomatous aquatic with oblong, floating leaves 6–20cm on long, submerged petioles. The flowering stalk bears a forked spike with 2 rows of numerous fragrant, white flowers, each with 1 waxy petal up to 18mm long, 8–16 stamens, and 3 or more separate carpels. **HABITAT:** Pools and ditches in southwestern Cape. **SIMILAR:** *Aponogeton angustifolius* is a smaller plant with leaves 5–10cm long and only 4–8 scattered, honey-scented flowers per spike, each with 2 petals 5–10mm long.

The fragrant flowers are an attractive sight in ponds and backwaters. *Waterblommetjie* is cultivated in the Western Cape for its edible flowers and fruiting spikes, traditionally used in *waterblommetjiebredie*, a mutton stew that includes sour leaves of *Oxalis pes-caprae* as another native vegetable.

♂S~   ♀<u>0</u>   Jun–Dec

Zantedeschia aethiopica
Arumlily, Calla, Piglily, Varklelie

 Rhizomatous geophyte, 60–100cm, with tuft of plain green, arrow-shaped leaves on spongy stalks. Small, unisexual flowers lacking petals are embedded on a slender, yellow, fleshy spike with female florets at the base and male above, furled around by a white, funnel-shaped spathe. Fruiting stem remaining erect, bearing a cluster of fleshy, orange berries. **HABITAT:** Widespread throughout southern Africa in seasonally wet vleis and streams.

A common garden plant and a popular and long-lasting cut flower, particularly for weddings and funerals. The rhizomes, although rich in oxalic acid and therefore toxic, are favoured by porcupines (hence the common names) but cause inflammation of the mouth in humans. The boiled leaves were used medicinally as a poultice.

Cyrtanthus ventricosus
Firelily, Vuurlelie

 Bulbous perennial, 10–20cm, with narrow, strap-shaped leaves usually dry at flowering. The hollow, purple-flushed flowering stalk bears a cluster of 2–12 nodding, tubular, vermilion to bright red flowers with long stamen filaments attached in lower half of tube. Fruits leathery, with flattened, black seeds. **HABITAT:** Cool, south-facing sandstone slopes on coastal mountains of the southwestern Cape, flowering only after summer fires.

A true fire lily, the flowers appear within a fortnight of a summer fire. Chemicals in the smoke stimulate the final development of the floral buds. The long stamen filaments attached towards the base of the tube are characteristic of the species and separate it from others with similar, gracefully nodding tubular flowers.

Dec–May   P6 St6 Ō

Gethyllis afra
Kukumakranka

 Bulbous perennial, 10–14cm, with spirally coiled, smooth or hairy leaves, dry at flowering. Flowers borne at ground level on a slender, solid tube; large, fragrant, cup-shaped, white with red on reverse, with 9–18 stamens, often in clusters, and the ovary buried in the bulb. Fruit cylindrical, like a small banana, protruding above ground. **HABITAT:** Sandy flats along southwestern Cape coast and near interior.

The fragrant fruits appear in early winter, and were traditionally used to flavour brandy and perfume cupboards. The short-lived flowers are produced en masse, possibly stimulated into bloom by a drop in atmospheric pressure. *Kukumakranka* is derived from the Khoisan name.

Dec–Jan   P6 St9–18 Ō

P6 St6 O   Jan–Apr

Haemanthus coccineus
Paintbrush-lily, Misryblom

Bulbous perennial, 6–20cm, with 2 or rarely 3 spreading or arching, glossy green, tongue-shaped leaves, sometimes fringed, and usually speckled with red beneath, dry at flowering. A stout, spotted flowering stalk bears a head of small, scarlet, funnel-shaped flowers surrounded by 6–9 stiff, red bracts. The fleshy berries are translucent pinkish. **HABITAT:** Widespread in coastal scrub and rocky slopes, from southern Namibia to Eastern Cape, often in large clumps.

Bulbs were used as a diuretic and fresh leaves as an antiseptic. The mature fruiting stalk topples over and the leathery seeds germinate as soon as the fruits have dried. *Misryblom* (manuring flower) refers to its appearance in the autumn when the lands are being prepared for planting.

P6 St6 O   Jan–Apr

Amaryllis belladonna
Amaryllis, March-lily, Maartblom

Bulbous perennial to 90cm, with erect tufts of strap-shaped leaves with a thickened midrib, dry or absent at flowering. The long, purple flowering stalk bears a cluster of several large, funnel-shaped, narcissus-scented, pink flowers on short stalks. Globular fruits borne on stiff stalks contain large, fleshy, pink seeds. **HABITAT:** Loamy soils in lowlands of Western Cape, often in seasonal vleis. Often flowering best after fire.

Both true amaryllis species are from southwestern South Africa, and most bulbs sold as *Amaryllis* are cultivars of *Hippeastrum*, a native of south and central America. Among its numerous common names are *Meninas para escola* ('Girls going to school', alluding to pink uniforms worn by schoolgirls), and the more direct Naked ladies.

Brunsvigia orientalis
Red candelabra-lily, Koningskandelaar

Bulbous perennial, 40–50cm, with 5 or 6 prostrate, tongue-shaped leaves in 2 ranks, leathery with red margins, dry at flowering. The stout flowering stalk supports a large, open head of irregular, red flowers on long spoke-like stalks, with unequally rolled petals and stamens flexed downwards. The fruiting head forms a large tumbleweed, each spoke topped with a 3-winged, heavily ribbed capsule containing fleshy, pea-like seeds. **HABITAT:** Sandy, mainly coastal, flats in southwestern Cape.

Pollinated by sunbirds that perch on the flower stalks, from where they can reach the nectar in the flower base. The anthers brush pollen onto their heads. The mature tumbleweed blows across the landscape, scattering seeds which germinate in time for the winter rains.

Feb–Apr   P6 St6 O̅

Nerine sarniensis
Red nerine, Guernsey-lily

Bulbous geophyte, 25–45cm, with narrow, strap-like leaves 8–20mm wide, dry at flowering. The slender flowering stalk bears a cluster of upright, flaring, red or strawberry-pink flowers with erect stamens clustered in the centre. The globular, membranous fruits contain small, pea-like seeds. **HABITAT:** Rocky mountain slopes in southwestern Cape.

The flowers are adapted to pollination by the Mountain pride butterfly, and the petals glitter in sunlight as if sprinkled with gold dust. The common name refers to the Channel Island of Guernsey, where they were introduced by the noted plant fancier, Major-General John Lambert, exiled there in 1662; they were not washed ashore from a shipwreck, as was rather fantastically imagined.

Mar–May   P6 St6 O̅

P6 St6 <u>O</u>   Nov–Apr

Agapanthus africanus
Cape agapanthus, Klein bloulelie

Evergreen perennial, 25–70cm, with strap-shaped leaves. The stiff flowering stalk bears a tight cluster of funnel-shaped, deep blue flowers 25–40mm long. The elliptical, 3-winged capsules are flexed sharply downwards, and contain flattened, black seeds. **HABITAT:** Rocky sandstone in cooler situations on coastal mountains of southwestern Cape, flowering mainly after fire. **SIMILAR:** *Agapanthus praecox* from coastal scrub and forest margins in southern Cape is a larger species with mid-blue flowers 30–70mm long.

Easily confused with its larger relative, this compact species with dark blue flowers is difficult to grow and is hardly known in cultivation; *Agapanthus praecox* is the widely grown agapanthus of horticulture.

P6 St6 <u>O</u>   Jul–Oct

Chlorophytum undulatum
Common grasslily, Graslelie

Rhizomatous perennial to 50cm, with slender roots and pea-like tubers, and narrow, fibrous leaves often minutely fringed on the margins. The unbranched flowering stem bears white, star-like flowers on pedicels jointed near the middle, each lasting a single day. The fruits are 3-winged and smooth. A little excavation around the base of the plant reveals the characteristic mix of roots and tubers. **HABITAT:** Widespread on stony flats and slopes in Namaqualand and southwestern Cape. **SIMILAR:** *Chlorophytum triflorum* from sandy flats along West Coast has hard, dark, tapering roots without associated small tubers.

Grass lilies can be confused with species of *Trachyandra* but always have tough, fibrous leaves and several floral buds arising from each bract.

Bulbine praemorsa
Common Cape bulbine, Slymuintjie

 Slender or stout perennial, 40–60cm, with succulent, channelled leaves, often with a waxy bloom. The yellow or orange flowers are borne in a loose raceme, each lasting less than a day, with fragile petals and bearded stamen filaments. The ellipsoidal fruits are borne erect on spreading pedicels. **HABITAT:** Common and widespread, mostly on rocky slopes in Namaqualand and southwestern Cape.

Plants tend to flower simultaneously, and on some days none will be in bloom. The leaf sap is widely used as antiseptic and emollient. Bulbines occur in both southern Africa and Australia, likely through long-distance dispersal of seeds from Africa.

Jun–Sep   P6 St6 <u>O</u>

Trachyandra ciliata
Cape-spinach, Veldkool, Wildeblomkool

 Sprawling perennial to 50cm, with fleshy, swollen roots and straggling, soft, spongy leaves that are channelled and usually hairy, and surrounded at the base by a papery collar. The white flowers are borne in an elongate raceme, each flower lasting less than a day, the petals with a pair of yellowish spots near the base. The fruits are pendent and 6–14mm long. **HABITAT:** Damp, sandy coastal flats from Namaqualand to the Eastern Cape.

The young flowering stalks make a tasty vegetable; harvest them before the buds open and boil or steam like asparagus.

Jun–Sep   P6 St6 <u>O</u>

P6 St6 <u>O</u>   Jul–Oct

Trachyandra divaricata
Tumbling starlily, Waaibossie

Stout, tufted perennial to 90cm, with slender, yellow roots and many fleshy, smooth, quill-like, bright green leaves individually wrapped with brown, papery sheaths at the base. The nodding, white flowers are borne in a widely branching panicle, each flower lasting less than a day, the petals with a pair of yellowish spots near the base. The hairless fruits are suberect and 10mm long. **HABITAT:** Coastal dunes and sand flats from southern Namibia to the Eastern Cape.

Tumbling star-lily is widely naturalised in the coastal districts of southern Australia and is a weed in places. The dry flowerheads act as tumbleweeds, scattering seeds across the sand. Plants are toxic to sheep and especially horses if grazed, causing paresis.

P6 St6 <u>O</u>   Jul–Oct

Bulbinella nutans
Marsh bulbinella, Vlei katstert

Perennial to 1m, with yellow roots and 5–13 bright green, narrowly channelled leaves to 25mm wide. The bright yellow or white, star-shaped flowers are borne in a conical raceme. The small fruits contain 1 or 2 shield-shaped seeds in each chamber. **HABITAT:** Damp, peaty soils or seasonal marshes in the southwestern Cape.

Marsh bulbinella can occur in dense stands of hundreds of individuals in marshy places, flowering after fire. Populations between Nieuwoudtville and Calvinia are bright yellow, but those on the Cape Peninsula and surrounding areas are white. A few related species occur in New Zealand, evidently the result of long-distance dispersal of seeds from Africa.

Kniphofia uvaria
Red hot poker, Torchlily, Vuurpyl

 Perennial 50–120cm, often in small clumps, with channelled, fibrous leaves that are keeled beneath. The nodding, tubular flowers are borne in a dense, oblong to globular raceme and are orange to greenish-yellow flushed reddish in bud, with oval floral bracts 3–9mm long. **HABITAT:** Near seeps, marshes and streams on sandstone slopes from Namaqualand to Eastern Cape. **SIMILAR:** *Kniphofia praecox* from the southern Cape is a larger species with longer, narrow floral bracts and prominently protruding anthers.

Red hot poker is widely cultivated, along with the similar *Kniphofia linearifolia*, and has become naturalised in parts of Australia, where it is regarded as an environmental weed. The tubular flowers are attractive to sunbirds and other nectar feeders.

Sep–Mar   P6 St6 <u>O</u>

Albuca flaccida
Common slimelily, Slymlelie

 Bulbous perennial, 40–100cm, with 3–5 fleshy, channelled leaves clasping the stem below. The open raceme bears nodding, fragrant, yellowish flowers with broad greenish bands, 15–25mm long; the inner petals have a fleshy hinged flap at the tips and the outer 3 stamens are sterile, lacking anthers. **HABITAT:** Mostly on coast in deep, sandy soils in the southwestern Cape.

The common name derives from the copious slimy sap that issues from any part of the plant that is damaged. There are several species with flowers like those of *Albuca flaccida* (inner petals with a hinged fleshy flap at the tip and the outer stamens lacking anthers) and the differences among them lie primarily in the leaves and bulb.

Aug–Oct   P6 St6 <u>O</u>

Albuca canadensis
White slimelily, Wittamarak

Bulbous perennial, 40–150cm, with the outer bulb tunics slightly fibrous at the top, and 4–6 fleshy, channelled leaves clasping the stem below. The cylindrical raceme bears weakly nodding, white flowers with broad green bands, 15–25mm long; the inner petals have a fleshy hinged flap at the tips and the outer 3 stamens are sterile, lacking anthers. **HABITAT:** Rocky sandstone or granitic soils from Namaqualand to the southern Cape.

A widespread and often striking species, sometimes forming dense stands along roadsides, with distinctive, weakly nodding green-and-white flowers.

P6 St6 <u>O</u>   Aug–Oct

Ornithogalum strictum
Clanwilliam chincherinchee, Vlei-tjienk

Bulbous perennial, 20–80cm, with soft, whitish outer bulb tunics, and 6–12 ±erect, lance-shaped leaves without fringed margins, sometimes drying at flowering. The glossy white flowers 15–20mm diameter are borne in a narrowly cylindrical raceme; the inner stamen filaments are only slightly broadened at the base. **HABITAT:** Clay or loam flats, often in seasonally moist sites, along the interior West Coast.

This and *Ornithogalum thyrsoides* are extremely poisonous to stock, which explains why they can form large colonies in pastures. The vernacular name *tjienkerientjee* is an onomatopoeic rendering of the squeaking sound produced when the stems are drawn gently across one another.

P6 St6 <u>O</u>   Nov–Dec

Ornithogalum thyrsoides
Chincherinchee, Tjienk

Bulbous perennial, 20–80cm, with soft, whitish outer bulb tunics, and ±7 erect, lance-shaped leaves without fringed margins, sometimes drying at flowering. The glossy white to cream-coloured flowers 15–20mm diameter are borne in a conical or rounded raceme and often have a blackish or brown centre; the inner stamen filaments have broad, membranous wings at the base that clasp the ovary. **HABITAT:** Sandy flats and lower slopes, often in vleis, from Namaqualand to the southern Cape. **SIMILAR:** *Ornithogalum conicum*, Summer chincherinchee, from the West Coast and Peninsula, has thread-like stamen filaments and blooms in summer.

The cut flower stems are tough and long lasting, and were a major export crop to Europe in the last century, surviving the sea voyage without damage.

Oct–Dec   P6 St6 <u>O</u>

Massonia longipes
Hedgehoglily, Krimpvarkie

Bulbous perennial to 5cm, with a pair of flat, rounded leaves pressed to the ground, the upper surface usually densely warty. The leaves cradle a cluster of rose-scented, narrowly tubular, white or cream flowers that fade to pink; the slender stamen filaments are joined at the base and bear small yellow anthers. The large, papery 3-winged fruits contain small, glossy black seeds. **HABITAT:** Sandy flats along the southwestern and southern coast.

The ball-like fruiting head with its winged, sail-like fruits breaks free from the bulb and is bowled along by the wind, scattering the shot-like seeds.

Jun–Sep   P6 St6 <u>O</u>

Lachenalia pallida
Viooltjie

Bulbous perennial, 15–35cm, with 1 or 2 plain green, lance-shaped leaves that are densely warty above or smooth. The shortly cylindrical flowers 7–9mm long are borne on short or long pedicels and are shades of cream, blue or pink with green or brownish markings; the anthers are included to well exposed. **HABITAT:** Often in large colonies in clay soil in the southwestern Cape.

This species now includes the lovely mauve-flowered plants common around Saldanha Bay that were previously recognised as a separate species under the name *Lachenalia pustulata*. The name *Viooltjie* (violin), probably originally applied to species of *Ornithogalum*, derives from the squeaking sound produced when the stems are drawn gently across one another.

P6 St6 <u>O</u>   Aug–Oct

Lachenalia mutabilis
Varicoloured lachenalia, Bontviooltjie

Bulbous perennial, 10–45cm, with 1 erect, lance-shaped leaf with crinkly margins. The stalkless, cylindrical to urn-shaped flowers 8–10mm long are borne in a tight spike and are pale blue and white with yellow tips, or yellowish green, with brown markings, always with several lilac to bright purplish sterile upper flowers; the anthers are concealed within the flowers. **HABITAT:** Sandy and stony slopes in Namaqualand and the southwestern Cape.

The reduced upper flowers are mauve to electric blue in some populations, providing a striking contrast to the lower, fertile flowers.

P6 St6 <u>O</u>   Jul–Sep

Lachenalia aloides
Capecowslip, Vierkleurtjie

 Bulbous perennial, 5–31cm, with 1 or 2 lance-shaped leaves, either plain green or spotted. The nodding, cylindrical flowers 20–35mm long are borne on long pedicels, in combinations of orange, red, yellow or greenish blue, with greenish markings; the inner petals are much longer than the outer and the anthers are concealed within the flowers.
HABITAT: Granite and sandstone outcrops in the southwestern Cape.

A beautiful species that is deservedly well known in cultivation. The various local colour forms are sometimes treated as separate species.

May–Oct   P6 St6 <u>O</u>

Baeometra uniflora
Beetlelily, Kewerlelie

 Erect, cormous perennial to 25cm, with several narrow, channelled leaves clasping the base of the stem. The flowering spike bears several yellow to orange, slightly flaring flowers 15–20mm diameter, with a dark centre. The long, cylindrical fruits remain attached to the dry stem.
HABITAT: Mainly damp sandstone and granite slopes in the southwestern Cape.

The flowers are adapted to pollination by monkey beetles and open fully only in bright sunshine. Many members of the family contain the toxin colchicine; Beetle lily is reported to be poisonous to cattle.

Aug–Oct   P6 St6 <u>O</u>

Wurmbea stricta
Waterphlox, Rysblommetjie

Slender, aquatic perennial, 20–50cm, with 3 quill-like leaves that are triangular in section, the upper two set just below the elongated flower spike. The pale pink, star-shaped flowers are 10–15mm diameter, with reddish marking in the centre, with 3 separate styles joined together near the base. **HABITAT:** Marshes and seasonal pools in Namaqualand and the southwestern Cape.

Waterphlox forms dense stands in seasonal pools and along streams, hence its Afrikaans common name *Rysblommetjie*, meaning rice flower.

P6 St6 <u>O</u>   Aug–Oct

Lanaria lanata
Kapoklily, Lambtails, Perdekapok

Tufted, evergreen perennial, 30–80cm, with fibrous, grass-like, channelled leaves that are finely toothed along the margins, and a dense, flat-topped, white-woolly panicle of small, mauve, funnel-shaped flowers, with the ovary below the petals. **HABITAT:** Clay and sandstone slopes in the southwestern and Eastern Cape.

This very distinct species, the only member of its family, is restricted to the fynbos belt in southwestern South Africa. Flowering is strongly stimulated by fire, at which time the woolly, white flower stems can blanket entire hillsides. When not flowering, the plants might be mistaken for large tussocks of grass.

P6 St6 <u>O̅</u>   Nov–Jan

Empodium plicatum
Autumn star, Ploegtydblommetjie

Dwarf cormous perennial, with narrow, pleated leaves up to 30cm long surrounded at the base by pale sheaths, often absent or just emerging at flowering. Solitary, yellow, star-like flowers are borne at ground level on a pale slender stalk more than 50mm long, with 6 long anthers clustered in the centre of the flower and the ovary hidden within the leaf sheaths at the base of the stalk. The leathery fruit remains at ground level. **HABITAT:** Damp clay and granite flats and lower slopes in the southwestern Cape.

The Afrikaans vernacular name *ploegtydblommetjie*, or ploughing time flower, is a reminder of the importance to early farmers of natural signs of the changing seasons, the flowering of Autumn stars coinciding with the onset of the winter rains.

Aug–Jun   P6 St6 Ō

Pauridia capensis
Peacock flower, Poublom

Cormous perennial, 10–30cm, with narrow, grass-like leaves, V-shaped in section. The flowers are solitary, often large, and yellow or white to pink striped purple on the reverse, usually with an iridescent green or dull black centre, and 6 long anthers. The slender flower stalks are subtended at the base by a single, large, leaf-like bract. They flex down immediately after flowering but later bend upright once more to loft the curved fruits above the ground, shedding their grain-like seeds through a lidded top. **HABITAT:** Seasonally wet clay or granite flats in southwestern Cape.

The flowers are mostly white or yellow, with dark markings or an iridescent eye, but pink forms occur around Tulbagh. They open only on warm days and are pollinated by monkey beetles. The species was previously known as *Spiloxene capensis*.

Jul–Oct   P6 St6 Ō

P6 St3 Ō   Aug–Jan

Dilatris corymbosa
Peninsula bloodroot, Rooiwortel

Rhizomatous perennial, 40–60cm, with a basal fan of narrowly sword-shaped leaves arranged edgewise to the grey-haired stem, and a flat-topped panicle of mauve, star-shaped flowers. The flowers have 2 stamens as long as the petals and the third much shorter than the petals. **HABITAT:** Damp sandstone slopes in the mountains of the extreme southwestern Cape. **SIMILAR:** *Dilatris pillansii* has all 3 stamens shorter than the petals, and *Dilatris ixioides* has the 2 long stamens twice as long as the petals.

The difference in the length of the stamens is linked to the economics of the pollination biology of the flowers. The longer stamens produce sterile pollen that is offered as a cheap meal to visiting insects, while the shorter stamen dusts visitors with fertile pollen.

P6 St3 Ō   Aug–Dec

Dilatris viscosa
Yellow bloodroot, Klamrooiwortel

Rhizomatous perennial, 45–60cm, with a basal fan of sword-shaped leaves arranged edgewise to the stem, which is covered in red, gland-tipped hairs. The dull orange or yellow flowers are borne in a rounded or flat-topped panicle, each with 2 longer stamens and 1 shorter stamen. **HABITAT:** Montane marshes and seeps in the southwestern Cape.

The vernacular name refers to the characteristic orange or red flesh of the roots and stem.

Wachendorfia paniculata
Butterflylily, Rooikanol

Rhizomatous perennial, mostly 20–70cm, with a basal fan of narrow, pleated, often hairy leaves arranged edgewise to the hairy stem. The apricot-yellow flowers are borne in an open panicle, each lasting a single day, the upper 2 petals with a dark marking at the base. **HABITAT:** Mainly in damp sandstone soils in the southwestern and southern Cape, flowering best after fire. **SIMILAR:** *Wachendorfia multiflora* has a short spike of yellow to brownish flowers with narrow petals and green bracts.

Individual flowers are either 'left-' or 'right-handed', with the style flexed to the left or the right and the lower stamen flexed in the other direction. This ensures that the flowers cannot be self-pollinated. The Afrikaans name, *Rooikanol* (red root), refers to the characteristic bright orange-red flesh and sap.

Aug–Dec   P6 St3 <u>O</u>

Wachendorfia thyrsiflora
Marsh butterflylily, Vleirooikanol

Robust, rhizomatous perennial, 1–2m, with a basal fan of broad, hairless leaves arranged edgewise to the stem. The golden-yellow flowers are borne in a dense, cylindrical panicle, each lasting a single day, the upper 2 petals with a dark marking at the base. **HABITAT:** Permanent marshes and streambanks in the southwestern and southern Cape.

A beautiful species that is almost mandatory for wetland gardens in the Western Cape, providing long-lasting spikes of golden-yellow flowers along streams and around ponds.

Sep–Dec   P6 St3 <u>O</u>

Witsenia maura

Witsenia, Bokmakieriestert, Waaiertjie

Slender, evergreen shrub to 2m, resprouting from a woody rootstock, with fans of tough, narrowly sword-shaped leaves. The tubular flowers are borne in pairs clustered at the branch tips, and are glossy, blackish-green with bright yellow, velvety petals enclosing and concealing the stamens. **HABITAT:** Marshes and seeps on the coast and mountains of the southwestern Cape.

One of a small lineage in the Iris family that are true shrubs, resprouting from a large woody rootstock. These highly specialised plants are found only on the Cape mountains. All other species in the family are herbaceous. The Afrikaans *Bokmakieriestert* derives from the resemblance of the inflorescence to the tail of the shrike-like Bokmakierie bird.

P6 St3 Ō   Dec–Oct

Nivenia stokoei

Stokoe's bush-iris

Evergreen shrub, 40–60cm, resprouting from a woody rootstock, with fans of sword-shaped leaves, and clusters of large, pale to deep blue or mauve, salver-shaped flowers with a tube 27–37mm. **HABITAT:** Rocky sandstone ridges in fynbos in the Kogelberg Mountains.

One of 10 species of bush-iris, all of which are local endemics restricted to a single peak or mountain range in the Western Cape. Together with two other small genera they constitute a highly specialised lineage of woody Iridaceae found only on the Cape mountains. The species was named for Cape Town mountaineer and plant collector, Thomas Stokoe.

P6 St3 Ō   Feb–Mar

Aristea africana
Maagbossie

 Small, often cushion-like perennial, mostly 10–15cm, with narrow leaves and flattened, mostly branched stems bearing small clusters of brilliant blue, star-shaped flowers enclosed by translucent papery bracts that are finely fringed and sometimes rusty brown at the tips; each flower lasts only a single morning. The fruits are short and 3-winged.
HABITAT: Sandy flats and mountain slopes in the southwestern Cape.

The short-lived flowers are visited by bees that collect pollen to provision their nests. Once this non-renewable reward has been collected, the flowers cease to be attractive and shrivel, to be replaced the following day by fresh ones.

Sep–Jan   P6 St3 O̅

Aristea capitata
Blue sceptre, Blou suurkanol

 Robust, often clump-forming perennial to 1.5m, with fibrous, strap-like leaves, and a cylindrical stem that is closely branched at the tip into crowded, overlapping flower clusters, each enclosed by dry, membranous and translucent bracts with dark keels. The bright blue, star-shaped flowers last only a single morning. The fruits are short and 3-winged.
HABITAT: Mountain slopes in moist places, 100–900m, in the southwestern and southern Cape.

An excellent garden plant readily raised from seed. A pretty, pale pink-flowered form is also available. Non-flowering plants can be confused with species of *Watsonia* but the leaves of watsonias have a distinct raised or thickened midrib whereas those of aristeas are completely flat.

Oct–Dec   P6 St3 O̅

P6 St3 Ō   Aug–Apr

Bobartia indica
Rush-iris, Blombiesie

Tufted rhizomatous perennial to 1m or more, with long, trailing, cylindrical leaves and a stiffly erect but otherwise similar stem bearing yellow, star-shaped flowers in a dense head comprising many individual clusters, the whole head subtended by a green, leaf-like bract with a long, needle-like tip. Each flower is carried on a velvety stalk that is concealed among the bracts, and lasts less than a day. **HABITAT:** Sandy flats and sandstone slopes in the extreme southwestern Cape, flowering mainly after fire.

Plants can occur in dense stands but flower well only after a fire. They can be a menace to hikers as it is only too easy to tread on the end of the long, trailing leaves, producing an unbreakable noose that trips the unwary at the next step.

P6 St3 Ō   Jul–Sep

Moraea fugacissima
Needle-leaved clockflower

Stemless, cormous perennial, 3–6cm, with a tuft of narrow or needle-like leaves. The solitary, bright yellow, cup-shaped flowers are carried on short stalks, with a 3-lobed, fringed stigma; each flower lasts less than a day, from ±10:30–16:00. **HABITAT:** Wet sand and clay flats in Namaqualand and the southwestern Cape. **SIMILAR:** *Moraea galaxia* has oblong to lance-shaped leaves.

Flowering is precisely timed, as if by a clock, and all plants in an area flower simultaneously on any particular day; on other days not a single flower is produced. Clockflowers were earlier treated in the separate genus *Galaxia*, named for their resemblance to a galaxy of stars.

Moraea lewisiae
Volstruisuintjie

Slender cormous perennial, 20–90cm, with 1–3 long, narrow, trailing, channelled leaves, and scattered, star-shaped, yellow flowers, each with the style divided into 6 thread-like stigmatic arms that spread between the anthers, and lasting a single afternoon, from ±15:30–19:00. The fruits are narrowly ellipsoid and project out of the floral bracts. **HABITAT:** Various soils and habitats, mostly in dry sites, from Namaqualand to the Eastern Cape.

Flowering time is precisely controlled and plants remain almost invisible among the surrounding vegetation until the yellow, star-like flowers unfurl in the late afternoon. The species is named for Cape Town botanist, Gwendoline Joyce Lewis (1909–1967).

Oct–Dec   P6 St3 Ō

Moraea miniata
Common Cape-tulip, Tulp

Cormous perennial, 15–60cm, with 2 or 3 narrow, trailing, channelled leaves, and star-shaped, usually salmon-orange or sometimes yellow or white flowers minutely speckled in the centre, with the petals spreading from the base to expose the stamens, which have their filaments joined into a column 6–8mm long that is hairy at the base, with small anthers 2mm long, each flower lasting a single day. **HABITAT:** Mainly clay slopes in renosterveld and in karroid scrub in Namaqualand and the southwestern Cape.

One of a group of related species that is poisonous to stock, and often proliferating into large stands in overgrazed situations. Flower colour is variable but usually salmon orange.

Aug–Sep   P6 St3 Ō

P6 St3 Ō   May–Dec

Moraea ochroleuca
Fragrant Cape-tulip, Aas-uintjie

 Cormous perennial, 35–75cm, with 1 or rarely 2 trailing, channelled leaves inserted on a straight stem, and cup-shaped flowers, either orange with a yellow cup or bright yellow, rather unpleasantly scented, the wide cup partially enclosing the stamens, which have their filaments joined into a slender column 7–10mm, with anthers 5–8mm long. **HABITAT:** Rocky sandstone slopes in the southwestern Cape, flowering only after fire.

The rather sour-smelling flowers are pollinated by carrion flies, which are avid visitors and lap up the nectar secreted at the base of the floral cup, becoming dusted with pollen during their visit.

P6 St3 Ō   Oct–Dec

Moraea ramosissima
Marsh moraea, Vlei-uintjie

 Robust cormous perennial, 50–120cm, with a basal fan of several to many narrow, channelled leaves and a well-branched stem bearing bright yellow, iris-like flowers with red anthers, each lasting a single day, from mid-morning to late afternoon. **HABITAT:** Damp sandstone flats and slopes, often along streams and in seeps, in the southwestern and southern Cape, flowering only after fire.

Plants remain dormant or unnoticed until after a fire clears the thick riparian vegetation, at which time dense stands appear in the late spring as a yellow froth along streams and drainage lines. The plants then disappear from sight until the next fire.

Moraea neglecta
Speckled quill-leaved moraea

Erect cormous perennial, 20–50cm, with a solitary, quill-like leaf and a rod-like stem that is sticky at the nodes, bearing large, yellow iris-like flowers with the nectar guide on the outer petals marked with rows of dark dots, and the style crests shorter than the style branches, each flower lasting a single afternoon, from early afternoon to sunset. **HABITAT:** Deep, sandy soils in the southwestern Cape.

One of three similar species of quill-leaf moraeas that differ from one another in details of the flowers, notably the markings of the nectar guides on the outer petals and the relative length of the style crests.

Sep–Nov   P6 St3 Ō

Moraea fugax
Edible moraea, Soetuintjie

Cormous perennial, 12–80cm, with 1 or 2 narrow, trailing leaves inserted on the stem well above ground immediately beneath the short, crowded branches. The large, strongly vanilla-scented, blue, white or yellow iris-like flowers last just a single afternoon, from mid-afternoon to sunset. The fruits are characteristically pointed. **HABITAT:** Deep sands and rocky sandstone and granitic soils from Namaqualand to the southwestern Cape.

The sudden appearance of the beautiful flowers in the mid-afernoon among the dry veld is an almost miraculous event. The starchy corms formed an important part of the diet of hunter-gatherers in the past.

Aug–Nov   P6 St3 Ō

Moraea tripetala
Fleur-de-lys, Blou-uintjie

Slender, cormous perennial, 20–45cm, with a solitary, narrow, channelled leaf inserted near the ground, and blue to violet, iris-like flowers with only 3 large petals; the stamens and style branches are separate almost to the base and tightly pressed against the stalk-like bases of the outer petals, and each flower lasts several days. **HABITAT:** Common and widespread in rocky sandstone and clay soils from the West Coast into the southwestern and southern Cape.

One of a group of closely related species characterised by similar flowers with three large, blue to purple petals, and the stamens and style branches separated almost to the base, not forming an erect column in the centre of the flower.

P6 St3 Ō   Aug–Sep

Ferraria crispa
Spiderflower, Inkpotjie, Krulletjie

Robust, cormous perennial, 40–100cm, with stiff, narrow leaves and an often densely branched stem. The many, shallowly cup-shaped, brown-speckled or pure brown, starfish-like flowers with crinkly petal margins are scented of cocoa and last just a single day; the stamens are united in a column in the centre of the flower and are overtopped by feathery style branches. The fruits are egg-shaped with a sharp point. **HABITAT:** Mainly on the coast in deep sands or granite outcrops in the southwestern Cape.

The curiously shaped and coloured flowers are visited by carrion flies that lap up the nectar in the bottom of the cup, attracted by the scent. They become dusted with bright orange pollen from the anthers that are concealed beneath the feathery style branches in the centre of the flowers.

P6 St3 Ō   Aug–Oct

Ixia paniculata

Long-tubed ixia, Pypkalossie

 Cormous perennial, 40–100cm, with a basal fan of several sword-shaped leaves oriented edgewise to the stem, and a spike of salver-shaped, cream to buff-coloured flowers with a cylindrical tube 35–70mm long that partially encloses the purple anthers. **HABITAT:** Seeps and streambanks on sandy soils in the southwestern Cape.

The species has escaped from cultivation and naturalised in some parts of Australia. Large stands still persist on Rondebosch Common but their native pollinator, a tangle-veined fly with a long, slender proboscis, is locally extinct there.

Oct–Dec   P6 St3 O̅

Ixia rapunculoides

Blue ixia, Bloukalossie

 Cormous perennial, 15–70cm, with 2–4 leaves oriented edgewise to the stem, the lowest large and sickle-shaped and the uppermost entirely sheathing the stem, and a branched spike of blue or mauve flowers with a funnel-shaped tube 6–15mm long that partially encloses the yellow anthers. **HABITAT:** Mostly clay soils in renosterveld in Namaqualand and the interior of the southwestern Cape.

One of a group of species with similar leaves and funnel-shaped flowers that partially enclose the stamens.

Aug–Sep   P6 St3 O̅

P6 St3 Ō   Sep–Oct

Ixia maculata
Black-eyed ixia, Kalossie

 Perennial, 20–50cm, with sword-shaped leaves oriented edgewise to the stem, and a compact spike of yellow to orange flowers with a large, dark centre that often has a yellowish, star-like marking in the middle, and a thread-like tube 5–20mm long; the stamen filaments are partially or wholly joined together and the bracts at the base of the flowers are rather papery and rusty brown. **HABITAT:** Granite and sandstone flats and slopes, mostly in fynbos, along the West Coast.

The common name is from the Dutch *kalotje* (skull cap), applied to the conical straw hats worn by Malay slaves in early Cape Town, which the flowers were thought to resemble. The dry, rusty brown floral bracts serve to distinguish the Black-eyed ixia from other yellow-flowered species with a dark centre.

P6 St3 Ō   Oct–Dec

Ixia polystachya
Cornflower, Koringblommetjie

 Cormous perennial, 40–80cm, with a basal fan of narrow leaves oriented edgewise to the stem, and a wiry, often branched flowering stem bearing a short spike of white or pink to mauve flowers, sometimes with a small dark centre, with a thread-like tube 5–15mm long; the small bracts at the base of the flowers are translucent. **HABITAT:** Granitic and sandstone slopes and flats in the southwestern Cape.

A variable, late-flowering species not actually found in wheatlands but named for the blue flowers that reminded early farmers of the true Cornflower or Bachelor's button of Europe, *Centaurea cyanus*.

Romulea flava
Yellow sandcrocus, Geelfroetang

Cormous perennial, 10–40cm, with needle-like leaves and a short stem usually branching above the ground, each branch bearing a solitary white or canary yellow (rarely pale blue) flower with a yellow cup and pale green reverse of the petals, with the stamens tighly clustered together in the centre. **HABITAT:** Moist sand and clay in fynbos and renosterveld in the southwestern and southern Cape.

Accurate identification of most sandcrocus species requires careful examination of the corm and is best left to an expert. The flowers of all species furl up at night and in inclement weather.

Jun–Sep P6 St3 Ō

Romulea rosea
Rosy sandcrocus, Froetang, Knikkertjie

Cormous perennial, 10–40cm, with a tuft of needle-like leaves and 1 or more flowering stalks bearing a solitary pink to purple or sometimes white flower with a yellow cup and purple feathering on the reverse of the petals, with the stamens clustered tightly together in the centre. **HABITAT:** Sandy and clay slopes and flats from the southwestern to the Eastern Cape.

The young fruits are juicy and were eaten by children. The vernacular name *Froetang* is a Malay corruption of the Portuguese *fruta*. A self-fertile variant with small, pale pink flowers thrives along paths and other trampled places and has become widely naturalised around the world.

Jul–Oct P6 St3 Ō

Geissorhiza aspera
Blue satinflower, Sysie

Cormous perennial, 10–35cm, with sword-shaped leaves that have the margins and midrib lightly thickened, and a finely velvety stem bearing a short spike of deep blue, funnel-shaped flowers with a very short tube 1–2mm long; the floral bracts are dry and brown in the upper half. **HABITAT:** Widespread and common, mostly in sandy soils in the southwestern Cape.

The Afrikaans name, *Sysie*, is also applied to the Blue waxbill, a pretty seedeater once commonly kept as a cage bird, and reflects the affection with which both species were regarded by the early residents.

P6 St3 O̅   Aug–Sep

Geissorhiza radians
Cocktail flower, Wynkelkie

Cormous perennial, 8–16cm, with narrow, longitudinally ribbed leaves that have the margins and midribs thickened and raised. Smooth stems bear mostly a solitary, large, deep blue, funnel-shaped flower with a red centre outlined with a white ring, and with a tube 6–8mm long and stamens that arch downwards and are bent up at the ends. **HABITAT:** Damp, sandy soils along the West Coast.

A charismatic species characteristic of wet places around Darling. The vernacular name alludes to the wine-coloured centre of the bowl-shaped flowers.

P6 St3 O̅   Sep–Oct

Geissorhiza imbricata
Pale satinflower

 Cormous perennial, 6–25cm, with narrow, longitudinally ribbed leaves that have the margins and veins thickened and raised, and a spike of large, white to pale yellow, funnel-shaped flowers, often flushed red on the outside, with a tube 2–8mm long. **HABITAT:** Damp, poorly drained flats in the southwestern Cape.

Still locally common on damp flats around Cape Town, but rapidly declining as its habitat is overtaken by urbanisation, agriculture and alien invasives – the deadly triad that threatens so many lowland species in the fynbos.

Aug–Oct   P6 St3 O̅

Sparaxis bulbifera
White sparaxis, Botterblom

 Cormous perennial, 15–45cm, with a basal fan of sword-shaped leaves oriented edgewise to the stem, developing cormlets in the leaf axils after blooming, and a short spike of nearly symmetrical, white to cream flowers, often purplish on the reverse, with a funnel-shaped tube 14–16mm long; a pair of dry, crinkly, fringed floral bracts encloses the ovary at the base of each flower. **HABITAT:** Seasonally wet, sandy or clay flats, often in roadside ditches in the extreme southwestern Cape.

White sparaxis is still locally common in seasonal wetlands and roadside ditches but it, along with many other lowland fynbos species, is becoming increasingly rare as habitat disappears under human expansion. Hybrids with other sparaxis species are popularly cultivated as spring bulbs.

Sep–Oct   P6 St3 O̅

Lapeirousia jacquinii
Purple painted-petals

Cormous perennial, 8–12cm, with a basal fan of sickle-shaped, longitudinally ribbed leaves, and 1 or more dense spikes of salver-shaped, dark purple flowers streaked with white and reddish marks on the lower petals, with a floral tube 30–40mm long, and floral bracts that are 2-keeled towards the base with narrow white windows on the sides. **HABITAT:** Seasonally moist sand in the southwestern Cape.

The flowers are visited by specialised nectar-feeding flies that extract the nectar from the bottom of the long floral tubes with slender, straw-like mouthparts.

P6 St3 O̅   Aug–Sep

Micranthus plantagineus
Combflower, Blouvleipypie

Cormous perennial, 25–45cm, with slender, quill-like leaves, and a dense, 2-ranked spike of small, pale to deep blue, funnel-shaped flowers. **HABITAT:** Seeps and other damp sites on granite or sandstone soils in the southwestern Cape. **SIMILAR:** This species was previously known as *Micranthus junceus*. The other two common species are distinguished only by their leaves: flat and strap-shaped in *Micranthus alopecuroides* and swollen and tubular in *Micranthus tubulosus*.

Combflowers can be recognised by their narrow spikes of small blue flowers in two opposite ranks. It is not always easy to distinguish among the different species, however, especially as they often hybridise when two or more kinds co-occur at a locality.

P6 St3 O̅   Sep–Jan

Thereianthus bracteolatus
Purple thereianthus, Persbergpypie

 Cormous perennial, 15–25cm, with narrow flat leaves oriented edgewise to the stem, and a dense spike of deep blue or purple, salver-shaped flowers with darkly veined petals and a slender floral tube 10–12mm long; the anthers are prominently displayed on filaments 8–10mm long. **HABITAT:** Dry sandstone slopes in the southwestern Cape, flowering after fire.

Thereianthus plants flower only in the summer following a fire the previous season, when they can be common on rocky slopes, but are otherwise not seen.

Nov–Jan P6 St3 $\overline{O}$

Watsonia marginata
Star-flowered watsonia

 Cormous perennial, 50–200cm, with a basal fan of broadly sword-shaped, often bluish leaves with thickened, translucent margins, oriented edgewise to the stem, and a wand-like stem with numerous short, ascending branches bearing spikes of bowl-shaped, pink flowers with a flared tube 13–20mm long and the stamens clustered in the centre of the flowers on erect filaments ±10mm long. The fruits are oblong. **HABITAT:** Sandy and granitic soils, often damper sites, in the mountains of the southwestern Cape.

Star-flowered watsonia is unique in the genus in having symmetrical bowl-shaped flowers; all other species have more or less irregularly funnel- or trumpet-shaped flowers.

Sep–Dec P6 St3 $\overline{O}$

P6 St3 Ō   Oct–Jan

Watsonia borbonica
Pink watsonia

Robust cormous perennial, 50–200cm, with a basal fan of rather soft, apple-green, sword-shaped leaves oriented edgewise to the stem, and branched, often purple stems with spikes of funnel-shaped magenta-pink flowers with a flared tube 20–40mm long and the stamens usually lying on the lower petals with filaments 13–20mm long. The fruits are oblong. **HABITAT:** Mainly rocky sandstone, and granite slopes, in the southwestern Cape, flowering well after fire.

The apple-green leaves and deep pink, funnel-shaped flowers are characteristic. Flowering is strongly stimulated by fire. The white form of *Watsonia borbonica* (long known as *Watsonia arderneii*), along with various hybrids, is popular as a roadside planting and in larger gardens around Cape Town.

P6 St3 Ō   Nov–Dec

Watsonia tabularis
Table Mountain buglelily

Robust cormous perennial to 1.5m, with a basal fan of sword-shaped leaves oriented edgewise to the stem, which bears conspicuously inflated, bract-like stem leaves and a branched spike of salmon-pink flowers with a curved, cylindrical tube 40–50mm long. The fruits are oblong. **HABITAT:** Rocky sandstone slopes on the Cape Peninsula.

One of several plant species that are endemic to (found only on) the Cape Peninsula. Restricted distribution ranges are characteristic of many fynbos plants, and a major reason why so many are now threatened with extinction.

Watsonia meriana
Buglelily, Waspypie

 Robust cormous perennial, 60–200cm, with a basal fan of sword-shaped leaves oriented edgewise to the stem, often with clusters of bulbils up the stem, and a branched spike of dull orange to mauve flowers with a curved, cylindrical tube 42–50mm long. The fruits are oblong. **HABITAT:** Sandy or granitic soils, often in vleis and streambanks, from Namaqualand to the southwestern Cape.

The buglelily can form dense colonies in seasonally wet places, proliferating by means of the numerous bulbils that are often produced along the stems. Such forms are a notorious weed in parts of Australia and New Zealand.

Sep–Nov   P6 St3 O

Pillansia templemannii
Pillansia

 Robust evergreen perennial, 60–90cm, with strap-like, loosely twisted leaves without a midrib, and a branching stem of large, bowl-shaped, orange flowers. **HABITAT:** Sandstone slopes around the Kogelberg, sometimes in large numbers.

A distinctive species without close relatives, flowering only after a fire the previous summer and then often in dense concentrations. It was named after the Cape Town nurseryman, Robert Templemann (active around 1881).

Oct–Nov   P6 St3 O

Babiana ambigua
Babiana, Bobbejaantjie

Cormous perennial, 5–8cm, with basal fan of narrow, pleated, soft-haired leaves oriented edgewise to the stem and often longer than it, and a short spike of large, fragrant, 2-lipped, blue to mauve flowers with white to cream markings on the lower petals, with a tube 10–19mm long. **HABITAT:** Sandy or gravelly flats and lower slopes in the southwestern Cape.

The corms are favoured by baboons and porcupines, hence the allusion in the vernacular name *Bobbejaantjie*. Easily confused with *Babiana nana* (see below), but the flowers are sweetly scented of roses and the inner floral bract (which lies between the stem and the ovary) is split in two to the base.

P6 St3 Ō   Aug–Sep

Babiana nana
West Coast babiana

Cormous perennial, 3–10cm, with a basal fan of often broad, pleated, soft-textured and soft-haired leaves oriented edgewise to the stem, and a short spike of large, fragrant, 2-lipped, blue or magenta flowers with white markings on lower petals, with a tube 12–17mm long; the inner bracts are forked at the tip. **HABITAT:** Sandy coastal flats and dunes in the southwestern Cape.

Easily confused with *Babiana ambigua* (see above), but the flowers are spicy scented and the inner floral bract (which lies between the stem and the ovary) is only shortly forked at the tip.

P6 St3 Ō   Aug–Sep

Babiana ringens
Rat-tail, Rotstert

Cormous perennial, 15–40cm, with a basal fan of narrow, very stiffly pleated, hairless or minutely haired leaves, and a cluster of flowers borne on a short side branch at ground level, with the main stem projecting vertically above it as a sterile stalk; the strongly 2-lipped, red-and-yellow flowers have a curved tube 30–45mm long. **HABITAT:** Sandy flats, often coastal, in the southwestern Cape.

This florally highly specialised species has the flowers restricted to a single short branch near the base, and the rest of the stem is reduced to a stiffly erect stalk that is used as a perch by visiting sunbirds, which otherwise also probe the flowers directly from the ground.

Aug–Oct   P6 St3 Ō

Chasmanthe aethiopica
Lesser cobralily, Klein piempiempie

Cormous perennial, 40–65cm, with a basal fan of soft-textured, sword-shaped leaves oriented edgewise to the stem, and an unbranched spike of orange flowers arranged in 1 rank, with the lower part of the floral tube twisted and then flaring abruptly and almost pouched above. The fruits are inflated and reddish purple within, containing pea-sized, thinly fleshy orange seeds. **HABITAT:** Mainly on the coast in bush and on forest margins, spreading by runners and often forming large colonies, in the southwestern and Eastern Cape.

The Afrikaans vernacular name is possibly an onomatopoeic rendition of the squeaking sound produced by rubbing the stems together. A good garden plant that attracts sunbirds to the flowers and, later, fruit-eating birds which disperse the seeds.

Apr–Jul   P6 St3 Ō

P6 St3 Ō   Jul–Sep

Chasmanthe floribunda
Greater cobralily, Groot piempiempie

Robust cormous perennial, 45–100cm, with a basal fan of soft-textured, sword-shaped leaves oriented edgewise to the stem, and a branched spike of orange (rarely watery yellow) flowers arranged in 2 ranks, with the floral tube flaring gradually above the almost straight lower portion. The fruits are small and brown, containing small, hard, reddish-brown seeds. **HABITAT:** Coast and inland on sandstone and granite in scrub in the southwestern Cape.

A good garden plant that attracts sunbirds to the flowers and, later, fruit-eating birds which disperse the seeds. The seeds, unlike those of the Lesser cobra lily, are small and dry without nutritious flesh, and possibly rely on deceit to entice the birds.

P6 St3 Ō   Jan–Apr

Tritoniopsis triticea
Wheat-eared reedpipe, Rooibergpypie

Stiffly erect cormous perennial, 50–90cm, with lance-shaped basal leaves that are narrowed below into a wiry petiole and dry, brown stem leaves that are drawn above into long stiff cusps, and a crowded spike of tubular, scarlet flowers with small petals and a tube 25–30mm. **HABITAT:** Rocky granite and sandstone slopes in the southwestern and southern Cape.

The flower spike, both in bud and after flowering, somewhat resembles an ear of wheat in its tightly overlapping bracts. The brilliant scarlet flowers, which stand out against the dry, late summer fynbos, are visited for their nectar by sunbirds as well as by the Mountain pride butterfly.

Gladiolus caryophyllaceus
Sandveld-lily, Sandveldpypie

Robust cormous perennial, 18–75cm, with hairy, sword-shaped leaves oriented edgewise to the hairy stem, with thickened, often reddish margins, and an inclined spike of large, carnation-scented, pink to mauve flowers streaked and speckled with red, with a funnel-shaped tube 30–40mm long. **HABITAT:** Sandy flats and slopes, usually growing in clumps of restios, in Namaqualand, the West Coast and the Swartberg.

Although the Sandveld lily has escaped and become invasive in parts of Australia, it is increasingly rare in its native country as a result of the demands of agriculture. The large fragrant flowers made it a popular cut flower in West Coast homes in early times.

Aug–Oct   P6 St3 Ō

Gladiolus carinatus
Blue Afrikaner, Blou Afrikaner

Cormous perennial, 30–60cm, with very narrow leaves oriented edgewise to the stem, which is mottled purple and white at the base, and an angled spike of fragrant, 2-lipped, blue or yellow, occasionally pink flowers, marked with yellow and blue on lower petals, with a short funnel-shaped tube 6–10mm long. **HABITAT:** Deep coastal sands, lower slopes from Namaqualand to the southern Cape.

In earlier years, when the Blue Afrikaner was still common on the West Coast, vases of its wonderfully fragrant flowers perfumed hallways and drawing rooms during the spring. A few people are insensitive to the violet-scented chemical ionone, which is one of the main constituents of the fragrance, and are unable to enjoy the scent of the flowers.

Aug–Sep   P6 St3 Ō

P6 St3 Ō   Oct–Dec

Gladiolus carneus
Painted lady

Cormous perennial, 25–60cm, with a basal fan of narrowly sword-shaped leaves oriented edgewise to the stem, and an inclined spike of large, funnel-shaped, pink or white flowers, often with dark pink markings on the lower petals, with a tube 20–40mm long that is about as long as the upper petal. **HABITAT:** Sandstone slopes, often in damp sites in the southwestern and southern Cape.

This variable species has flowers ranging in colour from white to deep pink, usually with conspicuous scarlet blotches or chevrons on the lower petals. These lipstick-like markings are the inspiration for the common name.

P6 St3 Ō   Nov–Dec

Gladiolus undulatus
Vleipypie

Robust cormous perennial, 30–150cm, with a basal fan of sword-shaped leaves oriented edgewise to the stem, and an inclined spike of large, long-tubed, greenish-white to cream flowers with tapering, often crinkly petals, the lower usually with red, lozenge-shaped markings, with a slender tube 50–75mm long that is slightly longer than the petals. **HABITAT:** Montane marshes and streamsides on sandstone and granite slopes in the Kamiesberg and southwestern Cape.

The unscented, long-tubed flowers are pollinated by long-proboscid flies, a pollination system that is uniquely well developed in southern Africa.

Gladiolus liliaceus
Large brown Afrikaner, Ribbokblom

 Cormous perennial, 35–70cm, with a long, narrow basal leaf with thickened margins and midrib, and a short spike of funnel-shaped, brown to russet or beige flowers that turn mauve in the evening and then become strongly clove-scented, with a long tube 40–55mm long; the tapering floral bracts are drawn into a slender point. **HABITAT:** Clay slopes, mainly in renosterveld in the southwestern and southern Cape.

A remarkable species with flowers that change colour each day, turning from brownish to pale lilac at night and producing a spicy scent that attracts the moths that pollinate them. The next morning the flowers revert to their drab daytime garb and lose their fragrance.

Aug–Nov   P6 St3 Ō

Gladiolus tristis
Marsh Afrikaner, Trompetter

 Stiffly erect, cormous perennial, 40–150cm, with a long, slender basal leaf that is X-shaped in cross section, and a spike of large, funnel-shaped, cream flowers, often with brown shading, that produce a spicy fragrance in the evening, with a long tube 40–65mm long. **HABITAT:** Marshy sites on sandstone, clay or limestone soils in the southwestern and southern Cape.

The large, pale flowers are wonderfully fragrant at night and attract moths as the pollinators.

Aug–Dec   P6 St3 Ō

Gladiolus merianellus
Flames, Vlamme

Cormous perennial, 30–50cm, with rather short, narrowly sword-shaped, hairy leaves oriented edgewise to the stem, and a short, erect spike of orange (rarely yellow) flowers with rounded petals, with a cylindrical tube 35–45mm long that is narrowed in the lower part. **HABITAT:** Sandy flats and lower slopes in the southern Cape Peninsula.

Endemic to the southern part of the Cape Peninsula, where it can be seen in the Silvermine and Cape Point nature reserves, flowering in the winter after a summer burn. It was previously known as *Gladiolus bonaespei*. The bright orange flowers are pollinated by sunbirds.

P6 St3 Ō   Apr–Aug

Gladiolus alatus
Kalkoentjie

Cormous perennial, 8–25cm, with longitudinally ribbed, sickle-shaped leaves oriented edgewise to the ridged or winged stem, and an inclined spike of fragrant, strongly 2-lipped, orange flowers with the upper petal held upright and the lower 3 petals bright greenish yellow in the lower part, with a short tube 10–14mm long. **HABITAT:** Sandy flats, slopes and plateaus in the southwestern Cape.

One of three similar fynbos species differing in details of their leaves and flowers. The curiously shaped flowers with their hanging, wattle-like lower petals have a wonderfully fanciful resemblance to little turkeys. They are visited by large, solitary bees for nectar.

P6 St3 Ō   Aug–Sep

Cyanella hyacinthoides
Blue lady hand, Blouraaptol

 Cormous perennial, 25–40cm, with a basal tuft of narrowly lance-shaped leaves that are sometimes velvety, and a branched raceme of unscented or fragrant, mauve or white flowers on spreading pedicels sharply kinked at the tips, with 5 smaller upper stamens and 1 larger lower stamen. **HABITAT:** Mostly clay and granite slopes, often in renosterveld, in Namaqualand and the southwestern Cape. **SIMILAR:** *Cyanella pentheri* from the Cederberg area has long, shaggy bristles along the leaf margins towards the base of the blade.

The roasted corms are edible and the vernacular name *raaptol* derives from their resemblance either to a turnip (*raap*) or a top (*tol*). Cast-off corm tunics have been recovered from archaelogical sites in the Western Cape.

Aug–Nov   P6 St6 Ø

Bonatea speciosa
Green wood orchid, Oktoberlelie

 Robust perennial to 1m, with oblong leaves crowded towards the base of the stem, and a cylindrical spike of green-and-white flowers that are sweetly scented at night, with the upper petals joined to form a small hood enclosing the solitary anther, and the lip divided into 3 narrow lobes, with a slender, club-shaped spur 25–47mm long hanging down from the base. **HABITAT:** Coastal scrub and forest margins from the Cape Peninsula to tropical Africa.

The fragrant, insect-like flowers are pollinated by hawkmoths that sip the nectar secreted from the long spur hanging down below the lip.

Jun–Feb   P6 St1 Ō

P6 St1 Ō   Aug–Oct

Bartholina burmanniana
Spider orchid

 Slender perennial to 20cm, with a solitary, rounded, hairy leaf pressed to the ground and a leafless, hairy stem bearing a single, large, white-and-mauve flower, with the upper petals forming a shallow hood enclosing the single anther and the fan-shaped lip deeply fringed into pointed, thread-like lobes, with a short conical spur pointing backwards from the base. **HABITAT:** Clay slopes and flats, from the southwestern to Eastern Cape, flowering mostly after fire. **SIMILAR:** *Bartholina etheliae* has the lip lobes expanded into spoon-shaped tips.

Nothing is known of the natural pollinators of this remarkable flower, and it remains an enticing challenge for a dedicated observer.

P6 St1 Ō   Sep–Oct

Pterygodium crispum
Crispy-leaved bonnet orchid

 Perennial to 40cm, with narrowly lance-shaped leaves with crinkly margins crowded towards the base of the stem, and a dense, cylindrical spike of small, fragrant, bright yellow, deeply hooded flowers flared outwards at the mouth. **HABITAT:** Sandy flats in Namaqualand and the southwestern Cape.

Like all species of bonnet orchids, the flowers have a strong, herbaceous fragrance reminiscent of fresh coriander leaves. They are pollinated by specialised oil-collecting bees that use their brush-like forelimbs to mop up the floral oils secreted by the lip, which they use for provisioning their nests.

Pterygodium orobanchoides
Barred bonnet orchid

 Perennial to 42cm, with narrowly lance-shaped leaves barred with red towards the base, and a dense, cylindrical spike of small, fragrant, yellowish-green, deeply hooded flowers with purple or black tips. **HABITAT:** Sandy flats in the southwestern Cape.

The bonnet orchids with deeply hooded flowers were previously placed in the separate genus, *Corycium,* but analysis of their DNA reveals a more complex relationship among the various species in the group.

Sep–Oct   P6 St1 Ō

Pterygodium catholicum
Cowled friar, Oumakappie

 Perennial to 35cm, with a few oblong leaves and an open spike of fragrant, yellowish-green, shallowly cup-shaped flowers, often flushed reddish, the fleshy peg-like central column curled over and minutely toothed at the tip. **HABITAT:** Clay vleis in renosterveld in the southwestern and southern Cape, flowering mostly after fire.

The Cowled friar is one of the more common orchids on the hills around Cape Town.

Sep–Nov   P6 St1 Ō

P6 St1 Ō   Jul–Sep

Disperis capensis
Cape witch orchid, Moederkappie

Perennial to 50cm, with 2 lance-shaped leaves inserted towards the base of the softly-haired stem, which bears a solitary, hooded, green-and-magenta or cream flower with conspicuously tailed sepals and a narrow, tongue-like lip flexed back into the hood and curled forwards at the tip. **HABITAT:** Sandstone seeps in the southwestern and Eastern Cape.

The curiously shaped flowers produce no rewards, relying instead on their superficial resemblance to the flowers of the Butterfly bush, *Polygala*, to deceive pollinating bees into visiting them.

P6 St1 Ō   Aug–Oct

Satyrium coriifolium
Orange satyr orchid, Rooitrewwa

Stout perennial to 80cm, with 2–4 elliptical to oval, leathery leaves clustered at the base of the stem and spotted with purple towards the base, and a dense spike of bright yellow to orange, hooded flowers, with the floral bracts sharply down-flexed in the outer half; the pouched lip of the flower is uppermost and ornamented with a narrow crest and bears 2 slender spurs 9–12mm long hanging down alongside the ovary. **HABITAT:** Moist clay and sand in the southwestern and southern Cape.

The bright orange flowers are pollinated by sunbirds that probe the slender spurs for nectar. Plants may form large communities on roadside banks.

Satyrium carneum
Greater pink satyr orchid, Rooikappie

Stout perennial to 80cm, with 2–4 thick, fleshy leaves, the lowest 2 somewhat spreading, and a dense spike of pale to deep pink flowers, with the bracts sharply down-flexed in the outer half; the pouched lip of the flower is uppermost, somewhat keeled and bears 2 slender spurs 14–20mm long, hanging down alongside the ovary. **HABITAT:** Sandy, coastal flats and slopes in the southwestern and southern Cape.

The pollen in an orchid flower is aggregated into a mealy or waxy mass. A single successful pollination visit is thus able to fertilise all of the ovules in each ovary, forming thousands of dust-like seeds that are widely dispersed by wind.

Sep–Nov   P6 St1 O

Satyrium odorum
Fragrant satyr orchid, Ruiktrewwa

Perennial to 55cm, with 2–6 oval to narrowly oval leaves, and a moderately dense spike of yellowish-green flowers, sometimes with a purple tinge, with the bracts down-flexed in the outer half; the sac-like lip is uppermost, with a narrow entrance, and bears 2 slender spurs 13–18mm long hanging down alongside the ovary, and the flowers are highly fragrant at night. **HABITAT:** Rocky slopes in scrub in the southwestern and southern Cape.

The flowers produce a spicy fragrance at night that attracts pollinating moths to forage for the nectar secreted in the slender floral spurs.

Aug–Oct   P6 St1 O̅

Disa bracteata
African weed orchid

 Erect perennial to 30cm, with narrow leaves overlapping up the stem, and a dense spike of small, greenish flowers tinged with maroon, with a narrow, hooded upper sepal bearing a short, pendent, club-shaped spur 3–4.5mm long.
HABITAT: Coastal fynbos, especially along roadsides and other disturbed places, from the southwestern to the Eastern Cape.

This rather dull little species has become naturalised in parts of Australia, aided by its easily dispersed, dust-like seeds and ability to thrive in disturbed places.

P6 St1 Ō   Sep–Nov

Disa graminifolia
Blue disa

 Slender perennial to 60cm, with a basal tuft of grass-like leaves that are dry at flowering, and a loose spike of blue to violet flowers, with a hooded upper sepal bearing a short, thumb-like spur 2–4mm long; the small purple petals have rounded, lime-green tips and the purple lip is rolled under. **HABITAT:** Sandstone mountains among rocks in the southwestern and southern Cape. **SIMILAR:** *Disa purpurascens*, which flowers in October and November, has a tapering spur and the margins of the lip are curved upwards.

The Blue disa is one of the great botanical rewards of a summer hike on Table Mountain. Its electric blue and purple flowers are pollinated by carpenter bees.

P6 St1 Ō   Jan–Mar

Disa ferruginea
Cluster disa

Slender perennial to 45cm, with narrow leaves in a basal cluster, dry at flowering, and bright red to orange flowers crowded in a head-like spike among dry bracts, the upper sepal narrowly hooded and tapering gradually upwards into a slender spur 7–20mm long. **HABITAT**: Sandstone mountain slopes in the southwestern and southern Cape.

Cluster disa is one of numerous orchids that deceive their pollinators with false promises of a reward. In form and colouring, its flowers resemble those of the Wheat-eared reedpipe, *Tritoniopsis triticea*, which secretes nectar as food for visiting sunbirds and butterflies. The Cluster disa provides no nectar and relies purely on deception to attact its pollinators.

Feb–Mar   P6 St1 Ō

Disa uniflora
Red disa

Erect or flexible perennial to 60cm, with narrowly lance-shaped leaves clustered towards the base, and a stout stem with 1 to few large, carmine-red to orange flowers, the upper sepal paler and streaked with red and bearing a wedge-shaped spur 10–15mm long. **HABITAT**: Wet cliffs, streamsides and seeps in the mountains of the southwestern Cape.

The Red disa is emblematic of Cape Town and the Western Cape. Like the Cluster disa, the flowers do not secrete a nectar reward, and rely on deception for pollination. The pigmentation of the flowers matches a range of other summer-flowering, nectar-rich flowers that attract the attentions of the Mountain pride butterfly, which is irresistibly drawn to objects of that colour, even scarlet clothing worn by hikers.

Jan–Mar   P6 St1 Ō

Kumara plicatilis
Fan aloe, Kaapse kokerboom

 Stout, regularly forked shrub or small tree to 5m, with tight fans of blunt, oblong, unarmed leaves at the branch tips, and short, rather loose racemes of nodding, tubular, scarlet flowers 35–45mm long. **HABITAT:** Sheltered sandstone slopes in mountain valleys.

The Fan aloe is one of just two species of *Kumara*, both restricted to moist sites in the Cape Fold Mountains. Traditionally treated as species of *Aloe*, Fan aloes are now segregated as a separate genus in recognition of their distinct evolutionary position in the family. The Fan aloe is slow growing and in cultivation should be kept clear of competing plants that may smother it.

P6 St6 <u>O</u>   Aug–Oct

Aloe microstigma
Karoo aloe, Karoo-aalwyn

 Stemless or short-stemmed shrublet, with a rosette of succulent, lance-shaped or triangular leaves to 50cm long, copiously spotted with white and with hard, reddish teeth on the margins. Bears simple, conical racemes of pendent, yellow to orange, tubular flowers 20–30mm long. **HABITAT:** Dry karroid slopes from Namaqualand to the Eastern Cape; especially common in the Little Karoo.

A floriferous, easily cultivated species that is attractive to sunbirds and other nectar-feeding birds. The leaves turn reddish when stressed.

P6 St6 <u>O</u>   May–Jul

Aloe ferox
Bitter aloe, Bitteraalwyn

 Single-stemmed shrub to 3m, the stems covered below with dry leaves and terminating in a large rosette of succulent, broadly lance-shaped leaves with hard, sharp teeth on the margins and often the undersurface; the candelabra-like flowering stalks bear 5–8 dense, cylindrical racemes of slightly upcurved, orange to red, tubular flowers 25–30mm long, with protruding stamens. **HABITAT:** Dry, rocky slopes in scrub and savanna.

An important economic species cultivated around Albertinia. The bitter, yellow sap that oozes from the cut leaves is collected and used in the purgative *bitter aloes*. The non-bitter, gel-like flesh is used in cosmetics.

May–Nov   P6 St6 <u>O</u>

Aloe mitriformis
Mitre aloe

 Sprawling, often branched shrublet with stems 1–2m long, covered with succulent, narrowly oval leaves sparsely speckled with white and with hard white teeth on the margins; bears branched, head-like racemes of drooping, scarlet, tubular flowers 25–45mm long. **HABITAT:** Rocky slopes and cliffs in the southwestern Cape.

An ornamental species that forms large colonies on rocky slopes. The leaves turn reddish when stressed. This species is also known under the name *Aloe perfoliata* but the correct application of that name remains to be established.

Dec–Feb   P6 St6 <u>O</u>

Ceropegia mixta
Variegated carrionflower, Aasblom

Creeping succulent with leafless stems 15–25mm in diameter, covered with conical tubercles loosely arranged in 4 rows, producing solitary, large, leathery, starfish-like flowers 70–110mm in diameter that are pale yellow speckled with brown, and foul-smelling, with a raised, shallowly bowl-shaped ring in the centre surrounding a complex structure comprising the stamens and stigmas. The large, erect, horn-like fruits are speckled with maroon. **HABITAT:** Mainly coastal on granite or shale outcrops in the southwestern and southern Cape.

The foetid-smelling flowers attract carrion flies as their pollinators. All of the stapeliads comprise a specialised group within the large genus, *Ceropegia*, to which they have now been transferred.

S5 P5 St5 <u>O</u>   Dec–Sep

Euphorbia caput-medusae
Medusa's head, Vingerpol

Succulent shrublet with a short, thick stem giving rise to a rosette of sprawling, warty, more or less club-shaped branches, 10–30mm in diameter, with small, narrow, rapidly deciduous leaves, producing a whorl of false flowers at branch tips, each false flower 10–18mm in diameter and comprising several minute, unisexual florets surrounded by a collar of fleshy, deeply fringed, pale yellow or cream and green lobes. **HABITAT:** Sandy flats and stony slopes in Namaqualand and southwestern Cape.

The plants exude a milky white latex when damaged. Each false flower is a cluster of minute florets surrounded by colourful nectar glands resembling petals. These attract insects, which lap nectar from the surface of the glands and pollinate the florets as they crawl over the clusters.

♂St1 ♀<u>O</u>   May–Sep

Cotyledon orbiculata
Cotyledon, Kouterie

Succulent shrublet with brittle stems to 1m and fleshy, broadly paddle- to spindle-shaped leaves arranged in opposite pairs, either smooth or velvety and usually with a grey bloom; a stout, erect flowering stem bears clusters of nodding, tubular, dull reddish flowers 10–30mm long. **HABITAT:** Widespread through western southern Africa in sandy or stony soils in scrub.

Plants root readily from cuttings. This attractive, drought-resistant species is widely cultivated in gardens and pots. It is highly variable in leaf shape, colour and texture. The sap is toxic to stock but is used medicinally.

Sep–Dec   S5 P5 St10 O

Tylecodon grandiflorus
Scarlet tylecodon, Rooisuikerblom

Succulent, often sprawling, shrublet to 50cm, with bright green, narrowly paddle-shaped leaves often rolled upwards along the margins, withered at flowering; an arching flowering stem bears somewhat 1-sided clusters of tubular, slightly irregular, roughly hairy, reddish flowers with a tube 30–40mm long that curves gently upwards. **HABITAT:** Rock outcrops, often granitic, along the West Coast.

The scarlet flowers are pollinated by sunbirds and are a striking sight among the dry summer fynbos.

Jan–Feb   S5 P5 St10 O

S5 P5 St10 <u>O</u>   Nov–Jan

Tylecodon paniculatus
Botterboom

Succulent shrublet with stout, peeling stems to 1.5m and deciduous, paddle-shaped, bright green leaves that are absent at flowering, having dropped off cleanly from the stem; a large, branched flowering stem bears clusters of nodding, urn-shaped, yellowish to red flowers with a tube 12–16mm long. **HABITAT:** Rocky slopes from Namibia through the Little Karoo.

The common name derives from the fleshy, slippery stems. The species is remembered in several place names, including Botterberg and Botterkloof. The plants are toxic to stock, causing *krimpsiekte*.

S5 P5 St5 <u>O</u>   Dec–Mar

Crassula coccinea
Red crassula, Keiserkroon

Shrublet to 60cm with opposite pairs of closely overlapping, leathery, bright green, oval to elliptical leaves, and flat-topped heads of tubular, bright scarlet flowers 30–45mm long. **HABITAT:** Sandstone outcrops in the extreme southwestern Cape.

The brilliant scarlet flowers attract the Mountain pride butterfly. This active, summer-flying butterfly has been colourfully described as having a passion for red, and is the sole or primary pollinator of several striking summer-flowering fynbos flowers, including both Red and Cluster disas.

Crassula obtusa
Jasmine-flowered crassula, Klipblom

 Sprawling shrublet to 15cm, the branches often rooting at the nodes, with opposite pairs of leathery, oblong to paddle-shaped leaves that are hairy on the margins, and small clusters of 1–5 tubular, white flowers, tinged pinkish, 30–40mm long and fragrant at night. **HABITAT:** Sandstone ledges in the southwestern and southern Cape.

The flowers are unscented during the day but become wonderfully fragrant at night, when they attract moths as pollinators.

Nov–Jan   S5 P5 St5 <u>O</u>

Tetragonia fruticosa
Seacoral, Kinkelbossie

 Sprawling shrublet, with long branches, often trailing through scrub, bearing alternately inserted, semi-succulent, oblong leaves with the margins rolled under; small flowers, 3–4mm in diameter, with 5 yellowish, petal-like sepals, are borne in terminal racemes or in the upper leaf axils. The broadly 4-winged fruits have small knobs between the wings, and become dry and papery when shed. **HABITAT:** Granite and sandstone slopes, especially along the coast, from Namaqualand to the Eastern Cape. **SIMILAR:** *Tetragonia spicata* is a stiffly erect shrub.

Sea coral is important in stabilising dunes along the coast. The leaves were almost certainly eaten as an antiscorbutic by early sailors. The winged fruits are adapted to wind dispersal.

Aug–Nov   S5 St~ <u>O</u>

S5 P~ St~ Ō   Nov–Dec

Mesembryanthemum crystallinum
Iceplant, Brakslaai

Robust, sprawling annual with angled stems and succulent, green or reddish, oval or paddle-shaped, often rather undulate leaves at the base, forming a small rosette, covered with large, glistening bladder cells; bearing loose clusters of white or pinkish flowers 15–30mm in diameter, opening only in sunlight, with 5 fleshy sepals and numerous sterile outer stamens resembling thread-like petals. The fruits are 5-segmented. **HABITAT:** Coastal sands in the Western and Eastern Cape.

The leaves and seeds are edible and the crushed leaves have some medicinal uses and may be used as a soap substitute.

S5 P~ St~ Ō   Aug–Sep

Cleretum bellidiforme
Livingstone-daisy, Bokbaaivygie

Tufted annual with mostly basal, tongue-like to paddle-shaped leaves, covered with bladder cells; bearing red, yellow, pink or white flowers 20–30mm in diameter, on slender stalks up to 25mm long, with 5 fleshy sepals and numerous sterile stamens resembling thread-like petals, usually with a paler halo and a dark centre. The fruits are 5-segmented. **HABITAT:** Mostly on sandy flats in Namaqualand and the southwestern Cape. **SIMILAR:** *Cleretum clavatum,* from salty flats between Darling and Hopefield, has very narrow, strap-shaped leaves.

A popular garden annual better known under the old name, *Dorotheanthus bellidiformis.* The vernacular name, *Bokbaaivygie*, alludes to the prevalence of the plants on the sands around Bokbaai on the West Coast.

Conicosia pugioniformis
Narrow-leaved iceplant, Varkslaai

Tufted perennial to 40cm, with a thick tap root and trailing branches radiating from the centre, with erect, succulent, narrow, 3-angled leaves; bearing solitary, large yellow flowers up to 13cm in diameter on slender stalks at the branch tips, opening in the afternoon and unpleasantly scented, with 5 fleshy sepals and numerous sterile stamens resembling thread-like petals. The fruits are cone-shaped with 10–25 segments. **HABITAT:** Sandy flats, mostly coastal, from Namaqualand to the Eastern Cape.

Narrow-leaved iceplant is invasive along the Californian coast. The long trailing stems sprout annually from a thick taproot.

Sep–Nov   S5 P~ St~ Ō

Carpobrotus edulis
Sourfig, Suurvy

Succulent perennial with trailing stems to 2m long, with straight or slightly curved, succulent, sharply 3-angled leaves with a rough keel and margins; bearing solitary yellow flowers 50–80mm in diameter at the branch tips, fading to pink with age, with stigmas about as long as stamens. The fleshy fruit is top-shaped and tapers gradually into the stalk. **HABITAT:** Coastal and inland slopes, from Namaqualand to the Eastern Cape, often as a pioneer in disturbed sites.

The sap is astringent and mildly antiseptic, acting as a soothing lotion for body and throat. The fruits are dried for jam and were an important dietary item among early residents at the Cape, appearing in middens and Khoikhoi burial sites along the coast. Cultivated to stabilise dunes.

Aug–Oct   S5 P~ St~ Ō

Lampranthus stipulaceus
Showy lampranthus

 Shrub to 1m with weakly spreading, cylindrical to 3-angled leaves that are shortly pointed and up to 40mm long; bearing magenta flowers 35–40mm in diameter in clusters of 3, with 5 fleshy sepals and numerous sterile stamens resembling thread-like petals. The small fruits are 5-segmented. **HABITAT:** Sandy flats along the West Coast.

A very fine, water-wise ornamental plant for sunny gardens, perhaps better known under its old name *Lampranthus amoenus*.

S5 P~ St~ O   Jul–Oct

Oscularia deltoides
Delta-leaved iceplant, Sandsteenvygie

 Sprawling or rounded shrublet to 20cm, with shining reddish branches and triangular, pale greyish leaves with toothed keel and margins; bearing clusters of pale pink flowers, with 5 fleshy sepals plus a single outer series of sterile stamens like narrow petals and numerous inner fertile stamens collected in the centre in a cone. The fruits are 5-segmented. **HABITAT:** Sandstone rocks in the Boland mountains.

Flowering plants are a striking sight in early summer when they ornament rock outcrops with cushions of glossy, pale pink flowers.

S5 P~ St~ O   Oct–Dec

Asparagus aethiopicus
Asparagus-fern, Foxtail-fern

 Spiny climber to 3m, with pale, ribbed stems covered with hooked spines and bearing stiff, peg-like false leaves in clusters of 4–6, with short racemes of fragrant, star-like white flowers. The fruit is a small berry, red when ripe.
HABITAT: Widespread in dry bush from Namaqualand to the Eastern Cape.

This commonly cultivated plant is not even remotely related to ferns. It is grown both indoors and in gardens for its ornamental foliage. The cultivar 'Sprengeri' is a scrambling form with sparse foliage, whereas the cultivar 'Meyeri' has erect, closely leafy stems rather like fox tails. The attractive berries are not palatable.

Jan–Jun   S3 P3 St6 <u>O</u>

Asparagus asparagoides
Bridal creeper

 Scrambler to 3m, with many small, spindle-shaped tubers arising directly from the rhizome, and glossy, oval false leaves, with solitary, nodding, cup-shaped white flowers in the leaf axils. The fruit is a small berry. **HABITAT:** Widespread in bush throughout southern and tropical Africa.
SIMILAR: *Asparagus ovatus,* from coastal scrub, is very similar, but has the spindle-shaped tubers developed well away from the rhizome at the end of slender roots.

Sometimes grown as an ornamental, its long-lasting foliage is popular as a filler in floral arrangements and bridal bouquets. Bridal creeper was introduced into Australia in the mid-19th century and has become a serious environmental weed there and in New Zealand.

Jul–Sep   S3 P3 St6 <u>O</u>

Microloma sagittatum
Arrow-leaved wax-creeper, Bokhorinkies

 Slender climber, with short-stalked, oblong leaves 7–35mm long, notched at the base with the margins rolled under; bears short-stalked clusters of tapering, green-tipped, pink to red, tubular flowers 5–11mm long, with narrow spreading sepals and pointed petals twisted together at tips. The horn-like fruits are usually paired and pendent. **HABITAT:** Widespread from Namaqualand to Eastern Cape in a variety of drier habitats, from rock outcrops to sandy coastal flats.

The small flowers are pollinated by sunbirds, which insert the end of their flexible tongue through tiny openings between the petals in search of nectar. Small parcels of pollen 'clip' onto the tip of the bird's tongue and are extracted when the bird flies off, to be inserted into the next flower that is visited.

S5 P5 St5 <u>O</u>   Jun–Oct

Convolvulus capensis
Cape bindweed, Klimop

 Sparsely hairy, perennial climber to 2m, with arrow-shaped to deeply lobed, often toothed leaves arranged spirally along the stems, and 1 or more white to pale pink, funnel-shaped flowers 15–35mm long in the leaf axils, with blunt, usually silky sepals 6–10mm long; the petals are completely joined in a 5-ribbed, funnel-shaped corolla that is tightly furled like an umbrella in bud, and each flower lasts just one day. **HABITAT:** Widespread on drier stony slopes from Namaqualand to the Eastern Cape.

Most South African bindweeds belong in the genus *Ipomoea*, distinguished by its knob-like stigma and including the cultivated sweet potato.

S5 P5 St5 <u>O</u>   Sep–Oct

Cyphia volubilis
Twining baroe

Twining perennial with lance-shaped to deeply lobed and toothed leaves, and showy, white to purple, 2-lipped, salver-shaped flowers 10–26mm long in the upper leaf axils, with the floral tube split down the sides and the stamens less than half as long as the floral tube. **HABITAT:** Sandy flats and slopes throughout the southwestern and southern Cape.

The tubers are edible; the vernacular name, *baroe*, derives from the original Khoi language.

| Aug–Oct | S5 P5 St5 O̅ |

Cysticapnos vesicaria
Balloon fumitory, Klappertjies

Straggling or climbing annual herb with brittle, 4-angled stems exuding a yellow watery sap when broken, and leaves with a greyish bloom that are often tendrilled and are twice-divided into wedge-shaped, 3-lobed leaflets; bearing short racemes of strongly 2-lipped, pale pink flowers with broadly winged, flaring petals 10mm long. The fruits are swollen and balloon-like, 20–30mm long. **HABITAT:** Climbs among bushes on sandy flats and slopes in Namaqualand and the southwestern Cape. **SIMILAR:** *Cysticapnos cracca* has smaller flowers 5–6mm long, and flattened, lance-shaped fruits 10–15mm long.

Fumitories are closely related to poppies and are sometimes included in the same family. The watery sap is diagnostic.

| Aug–Oct | S2 P4 St6 O̲ |

Dipogon lignosus
Cape sweetpea, Bosklimop

Woody climber, with the leaves divided into 3 diamond-shaped leaflets that are greyish beneath, the central one symmetrical and longer-stalked than the asymmetrical lateral ones; bearing long-stalked racemes of magenta or pink, sweetpea-like flowers 10–15mm long, with very short, blunt calyx lobes. The pods are oblong and woody. **HABITAT:** Scrub or forest margins in the southwestern, southern and Eastern Cape.

This decorative climber will survive more than a single growing season but is better treated as an annual.

S5 P5 St10 O   Jan–Dec

Bolusafra bituminosa
Tar pea, Teerertjie

Resinous, tar-scented scrambler, with hairy leaves divided into 3 oval leaflets, the central 1 symmetrical and longer-stalked than the asymmetrical lateral ones; bearing sparse, long-stalked racemes of bright yellow flowers 13–20mm long in the leaf axils, the calyx with long, narrow lobes. The pods are oblong, swollen, resinous and hairy. **HABITAT:** Mountain fynbos, often along streamsides, in the southwestern Cape.

The seeds bear a small waxy growth, termed an aril, that is sought after as a food source by ants, which carry the shed seeds into their underground nests, where they are protected from veld fires and well placed to germinate.

S5 P5 St10 O   Aug–Jan

Polygala myrtifolia
Myrtle-leaved butterfly-bush,
Septemberbos

 Sprawling or erect shrub to 2m, often velvety on the young stems, with scattered leaves that are variously ascending and narrow with the margins slightly rolled under or broadly elliptical and flat; bearing short racemes of purple, sweetpea-like flowers 12–15mm long, with the 2 inner sepals greatly enlarged like wings, the small side petals bi-lobed with the lower lobe much longer than the upper, and the large, pale, boat-shaped lower petal tipped with purple and ornamented with a brush-like crest. The flattened fruits are concealed by the dry, papery sepals. **HABITAT:** Rocky slopes in the southwestern, southern and Eastern Cape.

Scrapings of bark were whisked with water and this frothy liquid used by early Cape Malay people to anoint the dead.

Jul–Dec   S5 P3 St8 <u>O</u>

Muraltia spinosa
Tortoiseberry, Skilpadbessie

 Stiffly branched, thorny shrub to 1m, with short, spike-like lateral branchlets and small, oblong leaves; bearing purplish or pink-and-white flowers in the upper leaf axils, with the inner 2 sepals petal-like and much longer than the others, 2 narrow side petals, and a boat-like lower petal ornamented with a fringed, collar-like crest. The fruits are fleshy yellow or red berries. **HABITAT:** Sandy flats and rocky slopes from Namaqualand to the Eastern Cape.

Very beautiful when in full flower. The thinly fleshy fruits, although astringent, were eaten by early inhabitants at the Cape and favoured by ostriches and other animals, including tortoises, hence the common name *Skilpadbessie*, or Tortoiseberry. An infusion of the leaves was used medicinally as a tonic.

Jun–Aug   S5 P3 St8 <u>O</u>

S5 P3 St8 <u>O</u>   Sep–Feb

Muraltia heisteria
Purple gorse

Erect, usually sparsely branched shrub, with wand-like stems to 1.5m that are finely haired when young, and tufts of hard, lance-shaped, channelled leaves that are spine-tipped and often fringed along the margins; bearing small, purple flowers, sometimes with white side-petals, in the upper leaf axils, with a boat-like lower petal ornamented with a fringed, collar-like crest. The fruits are tipped with 4 slender horns.
HABITAT: Rocky, mainly sandstone, slopes in fynbos in the southwestern Cape.

Cultivated in Australia, despite the prickly foliage, and now naturalised outside Sydney. The species appears to self-pollinate. Flowering twigs were used locally as an appetite stimulant.

S5 P5 St10 <u>O</u>   Jul–Dec

Lessertia frutescens
Sutherlandia, Kankerbos

Single-stemmed shrublet to 1m, with the leaves once-divided into oblong, greyish-green leaflets that are hairless or sparsely hairy above; bearing short clusters of pointed, red flowers 25–35mm long in the leaf axils, with very small wing petals hidden within the calyx. The balloon-like pods are papery and hairless.
HABITAT: Sandstone and shale flats and slopes throughout southern South Africa.
SIMILAR: *Lessertia canescens*, from coastal sands, has broader leaflets that are densely silver-haired on both surfaces.

The leaves of *Lessertia frutescens* are widely used as a tonic under its old name, Sutherlandia.

Psoralea pinnata
Feathery-leaved bluepea

Willowy tree to 4m, with leaves divided into 7–9, thread-like leaflets to 50mm long that are dotted with glands; bearing small clusters of blue flowers on pedicels up to 25mm long, with a hairless or hairy calyx. The 1-seeded pods are gland-dotted and hidden within the calyx. **HABITAT:** Mountain fynbos, forest margins and riverbeds in the extreme southwestern Cape.

The seeds bear an oily outgrowth, termed an aril, that is sought after as a food source by ants, which carry the seeds into their underground nests. There the seeds lie protected from predators until the heat of a veld fire cracks the hard seed coat, allowing the embryo to germinate.

Oct–Apr   S5 P5 St10 <u>O</u>

Psoralea aphylla
Fountainbush, Fonteinbos

Erect, broom-like shrub to 4m with drooping branches and very small, scale-like leaves 5–17mm long present only on the young branches; bearing small clusters of blue-and-white flowers, with a hairless calyx. The 1-seeded pods are gland-dotted and hidden within the calyx. **HABITAT:** Mountain and lowland fynbos, often along streambanks in the southwestern Cape.

The heat of a veld fire cracks the hard coat of seeds stored in the soil, stimulating the germination of large numbers of seedlings with the onset of the next winter rains.

Sep–May   S5 P5 St10 <u>O</u>

S5 P5 St10 <u>O</u>   Sep–Dec

Aspalathus cordata
Heart-leaved Cape-gorse

Stiff shrub to 1m, with hard, oval to heart-shaped, spine-tipped leaves 12–25mm long that are 11–21-veined from the base, and bright yellow, pea-like flowers fading to bright red, crowded at the branch tips, with a hairy keel and white-haired calyx. The single-seeded pods are hidden within the calyx. **HABITAT:** Mountain fynbos on lower slopes in the southwestern Cape.

Many gorse species are pioneers of disturbed or recently cleared soils, deriving a competitive advantage over other plants from an intimate association between their roots and specialised bacteria that fix atmospheric nitrogen, as well as fungi that assist with the uptake of phosporus from the soil.

S5 P5 St10 <u>O</u>   Sep–Dec

Aspalathus crenata
Prickly-tea, Stekeltee

Erect or sprawling shrub to 1m with leathery, spine-tipped, oval to heart-shaped leaves 10–40mm long that are 7–11-veined from the base, with minutely toothed margins, and yellow, pea-like flowers fading to red or brown, crowded at the branch tips, with a hairless keel and hairless calyx. The single-seeded pods are hidden within the calyx. **HABITAT:** Mountain fynbos in the southwestern Cape.

Prickly-tea was used as a diuretic. Rooibos tea is another *Aspalathus* species.

Aspalathus astroites
Spike-leaved Capegorse

Erect shrub to 1.3m, with whitish-haired branch tips and leaves divided into 3 sharp, tufted, needle-like leaflets 6–15mm long; bearing small heads of bright yellow, pea-like flowers fading to orange, with a hairless, beak-like keel and hairless or sparsely hairy calyx with spiny lobes. The single-seeded pods are hidden within the calyx. **HABITAT:** Lowland fynbos in the extreme southwestern Cape.

Capegorse is a short-lived species that colonises recently burned soils but is succeeded after a few years by longer-lived shrubs.

Oct–Nov   S5 P5 St10 <u>O</u>

Aspalathus cephalotes
Violet-flowered Cape-gorse

Shrub to 1m, with leaves divided into 3 thread-like or very narrow, sparsely hairy leaflets 4–10mm long; bearing spikes or heads of pale violet or rose, rarely almost white, pea-like flowers at the branch tips, with a silky keel and a silky calyx with awl-like lobes. The single-seeded pods are hidden within the calyx. **HABITAT:** Mountain fynbos on lower slopes in the southwestern Cape. **SIMILAR:** *Aspalathus nigra*, with slate-blue to violet flowers, has calyx lobes mostly shorter than 3mm.

Most gorse species have yellow flowers; violet or pink flowers are exceptional in the genus.

Aug–Nov   S5 P5 St10 <u>O</u>

S5 P5 St10 <u>0</u>   Aug–Nov

Lebeckia sepiaria
Wildeviolette

Spreading shrublet to 50cm, completely hairless on all parts, with jointed, thread-like leaves; bearing long racemes of yellow, pea-like flowers with the lower keel as long as or longer than the standard petal. The narrow, many-seeded pods are spongy and up to 40mm long. **HABITAT:** Sandy flats, mostly above 300m, along the West Coast and in the southwestern Cape. **SIMILAR:** *Lebeckia plukenetiana*, from the West Coast, has the keel shorter than the standard petal.

Lebeckia is under investigation by West Australian scientists as a perennial grazing plant for arid lands.

S5 P5 St10 <u>0</u>   Jun–Apr

Calobota sericea
Silvery-leaved ganna

Shrub to 1.5m, with stalked leaves divided into 3 silky, elliptical leaflets that are folded along the midline; bearing stalked racemes of bright yellow or cream pea-like flowers, with the wing petals shorter than the keel, and a silky calyx. The narrow pods are silky. **HABITAT:** Rocky slopes in karroid scrub from Namaqualand to Citrusdal. **SIMILAR:** *Calobota angustifolia*, from coastal thicket as far south as Langebaan, has the wing petals longer than the keel.

Silvery-leaved ganna was traditionally used medicinally for colds in Namaqualand. It was previously known as *Lebeckia sericea*.

Wiborgia obcordata
Crested pennypod

Slender, stiffly branched or willowy shrub to 3m with velvety branches when young, and leaves divided into 3 wedge-shaped leaflets that are sparsely hairy beneath; bearing somewhat 1-sided racemes of small, bright yellow, pea-like flowers 6–8mm long. The flattened pods have a narrow crest along the upper edge and are 7–12 × 4–7mm. **HABITAT:** Sandy flats and slopes, from southern Namaqualand to the southern Cape.

Pennypods are named for their flattened, crested or peripherally winged seed pods, which are dispersed by wind. The seed remains within the woody pod until it decays over time.

| Aug–Oct | S5 P5 St10 <u>O</u> |

Cyclopia genistoides
Honeybush tea, Heuningtee

Erect, resprouting shrub to 2m, with hairless leaves divided into 3 narrow, needle-like leaflets with the margins rolled under, 8–30mm long, and clusters of yellow, pea-like flowers; the stamens, which are hidden within the keel, are separate from one another and not joined into a split tube as found in most other peas. The oblong pods contain seeds with a waxy appendage. **HABITAT:** Lowland fynbos on seasonally marshy flats and slopes in the southwestern Cape.

Cyclopia genistoides is the original *Heuningtee* (Honeybush tea), but today other species are harvested commercially. The shoots are chopped and fermented before drying in much the same process used to produce conventional black tea.

| Sep–Nov | S5 P5 St10 <u>O</u> |

S5 P5 St10 <u>0</u>   Oct–Apr

Indigofera filifolia
Willowy indigo

Erect, almost leafless shrub with willowy stems to 3m, the leaves mostly on younger plants or shoots, with long petioles 4–6cm long and divided into 6–8 elliptical leaflets that are sparsely hairy beneath; bearing white to pink or purple flowers 9–11mm long in racemes on stalks shorter than the leaves, with deciduous petals, the keel petal bearing a sac or spur on each side. **HABITAT:** Mountain and lowland fynbos along streamsides in the southwestern Cape.

The blue dye, indigo, was orginally derived from several unrelated plant species including woad, but mainly from the roots of the Indian species, *Indigofera tinctoria*. Its use dates back thousands of years, but the development of the synthetic dye industry in the 19th century resulted in the crash in indigenous production.

S5 P5 St10 <u>0</u>   Aug–Mar

Rafnia angulata
Inkpea

Erect or sprawling, hairless shrublet, with bluish-grey, wand-like stems to 2m and undivided, needle-like to oval leaves; bearing short racemes of 1–6 yellow flowers 8–20mm long in the upper leaf axils, with a sharp, beak-like keel and calyx lobes as long as, or longer than, the tube. The pods are narrow. **HABITAT:** Stony slopes in the southwestern Cape.

The common name derives from the propensity of the leaves to turn black on drying. The roots of some inkpeas were used as a liquorice substitute under the name *Soethoutbossie* ('Sweetwood') and a medicinal tea was prepared from the leaves.

Liparia splendens
Mountain-dahlia, Skaamblom

 Erect or creeping, resprouting shrub to 1m, with undivided, elliptical leaves that are 3- or more-veined from base, and large, nodding heads of 15–17 orange to red flowers 35–40mm long, nested among conspicuous, dark reddish-brown, leaf-like bracts; the calyx is pushed in at the base. The pods are oval or oblong, and the seeds are ornamented with a fleshy appendage. **HABITAT:** Mountain and lowland fynbos in southwestern Cape.

Plants turn black on ageing or drying. Seeds are taken by ants to their underground nests, where the edible appendages are excised, leaving seeds in safe storage until their hard coats decay with age or are cracked by heat from a wildfire. The flowers are pollinated by sunbirds, especially the Orange-breasted Sunbird.

May–Jan   S5 P5 St10 O

Podalyria calyptrata
Cape sweetpea, Keurtjie

 Small tree to 5m, with undivided, elliptical to oval leaves 20–60mm long that are silky on both surfaces when young; bearing 1 or more bright pink, sweetpea-like flowers 20–30mm long in the upper leaf axils, subtended by very broad bracts that are joined into a cap or sheath covering the bud. The silky, cylindrical pods contain brownish seeds bearing a pale, fleshy collar. **HABITAT:** Sandstone slopes in marshy places in the extreme southwestern Cape.

A fast-growing plant of great beauty that deserves a place in any garden in which it can be accommodated.

Aug–Oct   S5 P5 St10 O

Protea acaulos
Ground sugarbush, Aardroos

Mat-forming, stemless sub-shrub, resprouting from a woody base, with erect, hairless, narrowly lance-shaped to oval leaves 60–250mm long; bearing cup-shaped flowerheads 30–60mm in diameter at ground level, with hairless, green floral bracts flushed red at the ends; the slender florets are massed in the centre, with a wiry style 25–35mm long. **HABITAT:** Sandy flats and lower slopes in the southwestern Cape. **SIMILAR:** *Protea scabra* has rough, needle-like to narrow, channelled leaves, and the floral bracts are rusty-haired on the outer surface.

Flowering is stimulated by fire and blooms are seldom seen otherwise. The small heads borne at ground level are pollinated by rodents.

S4 St4 <u>O</u>   Jun–Nov

Protea scolymocephala
Thistle-head sugarbush, Witskollie

Erect, single-stemmed shrub to 1.5m, with hairless, narrowly spoon-shaped leaves 35–90mm long; bearing solitary, bowl-shaped flowerheads 35–45mm in diameter at the branch tips, with hairless, cream or pale green floral bracts; the slender florets are massed in the centre, with a wiry style 12–25mm long. **HABITAT:** Sandy flats and lower slopes in the southwestern Cape.

A pretty little protea for fynbos gardens. The small flowerheads are ideal for posies.

S4 St4 <u>O</u>   Jul–Nov

Protea nitida
Wagon tree, Waboom

Tree 5–10m, with hairless, olive- to silvery grey, elliptical leaves 80–180mm long; bearing solitary, cup-shaped flowerheads 80–160mm in diameter at branch tips, with short, sometimes silky, silver-grey floral bracts; the slender florets are massed in the centre and much longer than bracts, with a wiry style 60–80mm long. **HABITAT:** Sandstone slopes in southwestern and southern Cape.

Thousands of trees were felled annually in the late 19th century. The wood was used for firewood, charcoal, wagon parts (especially brake blocks and wheel rims) and furniture; the bark for tanning leather; and the leaves to make ink. As in all proteas, the wood is beautifully and finely speckled. The trees are protected from fire by their thick bark, resprouting from buds beneath the bark.

Jan–Dec   S4 St4 <u>O</u>

Protea cynaroides
King protea, Grootsuikerkan

Multi-stemmed, resprouting shrub to 3m, with hairless, paddle-shaped leaves 120–300mm long with a long stalk and an elliptical to rounded blade; bearing solitary, large, cup-shaped flowerheads 120–300mm in diameter at the branch tips, with pale or deep pink floral bracts that are often silky outside; the slender florets are massed in the centre and shorter than the bracts, with a wiry style 80–95mm long. **HABITAT:** Moist sandstone slopes in the southwestern, southern and Eastern Cape.

A very distinctive species instantly recognisable by its stalked leaves, the King protea is relatively distantly related to other proteas. It was declared the National Flower of South Africa in 1976 and appears on the Coat of Arms and as the emblem of the national cricket team.

Jan–Dec   S4 St4 <u>O</u>

Protea repens
Sugarbush, Suikerbos

 Shrub or tree to 4.5m, with hairless, narrow to spoon-shaped leaves 50–150mm long; bearing solitary, narrowly cup-shaped flowerheads 100–160mm long at the branch tips, with pale yellow to red, or bicoloured, floral bracts covered with a sticky gum; the slender florets are massed in the centre and shorter than the bracts, with a wiry style 70–90mm long. **HABITAT:** Sandstone and clay flats and slopes from the West Coast to the southern and Eastern Cape.

The vernacular name refers to the copious sugary nectar contained in the flowerheads, which was collected and boiled down to make a syrup (*bossiestroop*). The Sugarbush also features in a traditional Afrikaans folk song of the same name, as a term of endearment for a sweetheart.

S4 St4 <u>O</u>   Jan–Dec

Protea obtusifolia
Limestone sugarbush

 Large shrub to 4m, with elliptical to lance-shaped leaves 100–150mm long, curved upwards and tapering at the base, hairless when mature; bearing solitary, narrowly cup-shaped flowerheads 90–120 × 50–80mm, with downy, cream to red floral bracts, the inner ones spoon-shaped; the slender florets are massed in the centre and shorter than the bracts, with a wiry style ±65mm long. **HABITAT:** Limestone flats and hills on the Agulhas Plain. **SIMILAR:** *Protea susannae* from the same area has leaves with an unpleasant, sulphurous odour and slightly broader flowerheads with the bracts covered in a sticky brown varnish.

This attractive species is cultivated for the cut flower market and is a parent of several commercial hybrids.

S4 St4 <u>O</u>   Apr–Sep

Protea compacta
Bot River sugarbush

Lanky shrub to 3.5m with oblong to oval leaves 50–130mm long, curved upwards and lobed at the base, hairless when mature; bearing narrowly cup-shaped flowerheads 90–120 × 70–100mm with downy pink or white involucral bracts, the inner ones spoon-shaped; the slender florets are massed in the centre and shorter than the bracts, with a wiry style 60–70mm long. **HABITAT:** Coastal slopes and flats in the extreme southwestern Cape. **SIMILAR:** *Protea eximia* from the southern Cape has the florets tipped with velvety black or brown hairs.

One of the best known of the species cultivated for the cut flower market on account of its long, straight branches. It is a parent of several commercial hybrids.

| Apr–Sep | S4 St4 <u>O</u> |

Protea neriifolia
Oleander-leaved protea, Baardsuikerbos

Shrub to 3m, with oblong, green leaves 100–180mm long, hairless when mature; bearing cylindrical flowerheads 100–130mm long with silky, cream to pink floral bracts, the outer ones with hard, brown margins and the inner ones with a dense, white or black beard and fine, silvery hairs below the beard; the slender florets are massed in the centre and shorter than the bracts, with a wiry style 55–70mm long. **HABITAT:** Sandstone and clay slopes in the southwestern, southern and Eastern Cape. **SIMILAR:** *Protea laurifolia*, the Laurel-leaved protea, is distinguished by its greyish, elliptical leaves and slightly more northerly distribution.

| Feb–Nov | S4 St4 <u>O</u> |

S4 St4 <u>O</u>   Apr–Sep

Protea coronata
Green protea, Groenhofiesuikerbos

Erect shrub or small tree to 5m, with hairless or silky, elliptical, green leaves 70–120mm long; bearing solitary, cylindrical flowerheads ±100mm long at the branch tips, with apple-green involucral bracts, the tips curved inwards and fringed with a white beard; the slender florets are massed in the centre and shorter than the bracts, with a wiry style ±60mm long. **HABITAT:** Clay slopes in the southwestern, southern and Eastern Cape.

The Green protea is unusual among proteas in growing on granite or shale soils rather than those derived from sandstone or limestone. The fresh blooms are used as cut flowers and the old, woody bases of the heads are dried and sold as 'protea rosettes' or 'protea daisies' for dried arrangements and Christmas wreaths.

S4 St4 <u>O</u>   Jun–Jan

Protea magnifica
Queen protea

Sprawling, single-stemmed shrub to 2.5m, with oblong, grey leaves 100–210mm long that have undulating, hard, red or yellow margins; bearing large cup-shaped flowerheads 140mm long, with silky, pink or cream bracts curved back at tips with a dense white or black beard; the slender florets are massed in the centre and shorter than the bracts, with brown or black velvety tips, and a wiry style 60–70mm long. **HABITAT:** Sandstone slopes in southwestern Cape.

Only the King protea is larger than the Queen protea. Favouring rock outcrops on steep slopes at higher altitudes, where they are protected from fires, the species is not commonly seen but is an unforgettable sight. It is much in demand for the cut flower trade, and has been hybridised with several other species.

Aulax cancellata
Featherbush

 Single-stemmed shrub to 2.5m, with needle-like or very narrow, channelled leaves. The sexes are on separate plants: the pale yellow male florets in loose spikes at the branch tips, and the female florets in protea-like heads surrounded by leafy, yellowish green floral bracts. **HABITAT:** Sandstone slopes in the southwestern and southern Cape. **SIMILAR:** One of three rather similar-looking species: *Aulax umbellata* from the Overberg is also single-stemmed but has narrowly paddle-shaped leaves, and *Aulax pallasia* is a multi-stemmed shrub resprouting from a large, woody rootstock, with narrow, flat leaves.

Nov–Feb   ♂S4 St4   ♀S4 0

Leucadendron sessile
Western sunbush

 Single-stemmed shrub to 1.5m, with hairless, narrowly elliptical leaves up to 64mm long on male plants and up to 80mm long on female plants; the floral leaves of similar shape and size, but coloured yellow or red. The sexes are on separate plants with lemon-scented florets: male flowerheads ±35mm in diameter with erect, brown, scale-like bracts around them, and female heads 14–18mm in diameter. The scales on the fruiting cones recurve and open within the same season to shed the fruits. **HABITAT:** Granitic slopes and flats in the southwestern Cape; especially visible on Sir Lowry's Pass.

Jul–Aug   ♂S4 St4   ♀S4 0

Leucadendron argenteum
Silvertree, Witteboom

Tree to 10m with silver-silky, lance-shaped leaves to 150mm with fringed margins, and similar floral leaves. The sexes are on separate plants: male flowerheads ±50mm in diameter and female flowerheads ±40mm in diameter. The scales on the fruiting cones are tightly closed, retaining the seeds for several seasons until the parent plant dies. **HABITAT:** Granite and clay slopes from Cape Peninsula to Somerset West.

Extensively exploited for firewood in the 17th and 18th centuries and now much reduced in numbers. The Witteboome railway station on the southern line reminds us of its prevalence. The seeds are released from the woody cones after the trees die through age or fire, falling en masse onto the newly cleared and fertilised soil.

♂S4 St4 ♀S4 O   Sep–Oct

Leucadendron rubrum
Spinning top, Tolletjiesbos

Single-stemmed shrub to 2.5m, with paddle-shaped leaves up to 34mm long on male plants and up to 70mm long on female plants, hairless when mature and with similar floral leaves. The sexes are on separate plants: male flowerheads ±5mm in diameter in clusters of up to 16 heads, and female heads solitary and ±20mm in diameter, top-shaped with brown-edged bracts. The scales on the fruiting cones remain tightly closed, retaining seeds for several seasons until the parent plant dies. **HABITAT:** Sandstone slopes in the southwestern and southern Cape.

The vernacular name, *Tolbos* ('Spinning top bush'), alludes to the tendency of the woody cones of many species to spin like a top when dropped or kicked, and probably not to any resemblance to the toy itself.

♂S4 St4 ♀S4 O   Aug–Sep

Leucadendron salicifolium
Common stream conebush, Riviertolbos

 Single-stemmed shrub to 3m, with hairless, narrowly sickle-shaped leaves that are twisted below and up to 60mm long, and a few similar-shaped, creamy yellow floral leaves. The sexes are on separate plants with slightly fruit-scented florets in flowerheads 9–10mm in diameter: the male heads at the ends of numerous short branches forming large clusters, and the female head solitary at the branch tips. The scales on the fruiting cones remain tightly closed, retaining the seeds for several seasons until the parent plant dies. **HABITAT:** Near streams and seeps on flats and slopes in the southwestern Cape.

Jul–Sep ♂S4 St4 ♀S4 <u>0</u>

Leucadendron salignum
Common sunshine conebush, Knoppiesgeelbos

 Sprawling or erect, resprouting shrub with many stems up to 2m, and hairless, narrowly paddle-shaped leaves that are twisted below and 20–47mm long on male plants and 48–58mm long on female plants; the male floral leaves are slightly longer and yellow or sometimes red, and the female floral leaves are larger and ivory or red. The sexes are on separate plants with sweetly or yeast-scented florets in solitary heads at the branch tips: the male flowerheads 10–14mm in diameter and the female heads 9–12mm in diameter. The scales on the fruiting cones remain tightly closed, retaining the seeds for several seasons until the parent plant dies. **HABITAT:** Sandy and clay slopes and flats throughout the southwestern and southern Cape.

Apr–Nov ♂S4 St4 ♀S4 <u>0</u>

Leucadendron coniferum
Dune conebush, Duinegeelbos

Shrub or small tree to 4m, with twisted, narrowly paddle-shaped leaves up to 77mm long on male plants and up to 83mm long on female plants, hairless when mature, and yellow floral leaves broadened below. The sexes are on separate plants: male flowerheads ±18mm in diameter and female heads ±14mm in diameter. The scales on the fruiting cones remain tightly closed, retaining the seeds for several seasons until the parent plant dies. **HABITAT:** Coastal sands in the extreme southwestern Cape.

♂S4 St4 ♀S4 <u>0</u>   Aug–Sep

Leucadendron laureolum
Golden conebush, Louriertolbos

Single-stemmed shrub to 2m, with oblong leaves up to 75mm long on male plants and up to 95mm long on female plants, hairless when mature, and larger, yellow floral leaves that conceal the young heads. The sexes are on separate plants with slightly fruit-scented florets in solitary heads at the branch tips: male flowerheads ±20mm in diameter and female heads ±14mm in diameter. The cones have a spiral of 8 shallow grooves, and the scales on the fruiting cones remain tightly closed, retaining the seeds for several seasons until the parent plant dies. **HABITAT:** Sandstone slopes in the extreme southwestern Cape.

♂S4 St4 ♀S4 <u>0</u>   Jun–Jul

Mimetes hirtus
Marsh pagoda, Vleistompie

Single-stemmed shrub to 2m, with almost hairless, oval to lance-shaped leaves 25–45mm long with a solitary tooth at the tip and similar inflorescence leaves. The flower spikes comprise headlets of 9–14 white flowers surrounded by bright yellow floral bracts with red tips; the style is red and 50–55mm long. **HABITAT:** Peaty marshes in the extreme southwestern Cape.

The red-and-yellow flower spikes are visited by sunbirds and sugarbirds. Much of the lowland habitat in which the Marsh pagoda grows has disappeared.

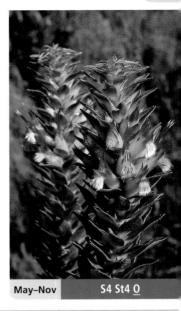

May–Nov   S4 St4 <u>O</u>

Mimetes cucullatus
Common pagoda, Rooistompie

Multi-stemmed shrub to 1.4m, resprouting from a woody base, with hairless, oblong to elliptical leaves 25–55mm long with more than 1 tooth at the tip and spoon-shaped red inflorescence leaves. The flower spikes comprise headlets of 4–7 white flowers surrounded by small bracts; the style is red and 45–50mm long. **HABITAT:** Sandstone slopes and flats mainly in the southwestern and southern Cape.

The only species of pagoda that resprouts after fire, sending up stems from a woody rootstock. Individuals of other species are killed by fire and the population must regenerate through the germination of soil-stored seeds. The vernacular name *stompie*, also applied to *Brunia*, refers to the stumps remaining after the woody shrubs have burnt in periodic veld fires.

Jan–Dec   S4 St4 <u>O</u>

Mimetes fimbriifolius
Tree pagoda, Kreupelboom

 Tree to 4m with oblong to elliptical leaves 40–70mm long, densely fringed with hairs and with more than 1 tooth at the tip, and dull reddish-yellow, spoon-shaped inflorescence leaves. The flower spikes comprise headlets of 4–7 white flowers surrounded by small bracts; the style is yellow with a red tip and 55–60mm long. **HABITAT:** Rocky slopes on the Cape Peninsula.

The Tree pagoda is found only on the Cape Peninsula and was once harvested for firewood. Good populations now survive only on the Southern Peninsula, especially in Silvermine and Cape Point.

S4 St4 <u>O</u>   Jan–Dec

Serruria fasciflora
Common pin spiderhead

 Sprawling to erect shrublet to 1m, with sparsely hairy leaves 30–70mm long, finely divided into 10–15 needle-like segments; bearing clusters of many flowerheads on a short, hairy stalk, each head containing 5–7 sweetly scented, silvery pink flowers that are straight in bud like matchsticks; the style is 5–7mm long. **HABITAT:** Sandy flats and lower slopes in the southwestern Cape. **SIMILAR:** Blushing bride, *Serruria florida,* has the flowerheads surrounded by conspicuous pale pink bracts.

The silvery hairs on the floral buds shine like burnished metal.

S4 St4 <u>O</u>   Jan–Dec

Serruria villosa
Golden spiderhead, Gouespinnekopbos

Compact, rounded shrublet to 80cm with silky leaves 20–40mm long, finely divided into 16–18 needle-like segments; bears a solitary, stalkless flowerhead nested among the leaves at the branch tips, the head containing 18–22 fragrant yellow flowers that are straight in bud like matchsticks; the style is ±10mm long.
HABITAT: Sandstone slopes and flats on the southern Cape Peninsula.

Golden spiderhead is one of several plant species found only on the Cape Peninsula. Its yellow flowers are unusual for the genus, in which pink flowers are usual.

| Apr–Jul | S4 St4 <u>O</u> |

Leucospermum oleifolium
Overberg pincushion

Rounded shrub to 1m, with hairless or hairy, oval to lance-shaped leaves 40–60mm long, tipped with 1–5 hard teeth; bearing clusters of up to 5 flat-topped flowerheads 25–40mm in diameter at the branch tips, yellow-green, fading to red; the style is straight and 25–30mm long.
HABITAT: Sandstone slopes in the extreme southwestern Cape.

This is a charming and rewarding species for small gardens, and can be propagated by seed or cuttings.

| Aug–Jan | S4 St4 <u>O</u> |

Leucospermum calligerum
Arid pincushion, Luisiesbos

Shrub to 2m, with grey-haired, lance-shaped to elliptical leaves, 12–36mm long, mostly tipped with a hard tooth; bearing clusters of 2–6 globular flowerheads 20–35mm in diameter at the branch tips, cream-coloured, fading to dull red; the style is slightly curved inwards and 21–25mm long. **HABITAT:** Dry, sandy slopes in the southwestern Cape.

The vernacular name, *Luisiesbos* ('Lice bush'), refers to the resemblance of the nutlets to lice, a salutary indication of how familiar the early settlers were with those particular vermin.

S4 St4 O   Jul–Jan

Leucospermum bolusii
Gordon's Bay pincushion, Witluisie

Rounded shrub to 1.5m, with almost hairless, oval to elliptical leaves, 25–45mm long, tipped with a hard tooth; bearing clusters of up to 8 rounded flowerheads ±20mm in diameter at the branch tips, cream-coloured, fading to pale pink; the style is straight and 15–20mm long. **HABITAT:** Rocky sandstone slopes above Gordon's Bay. A very local species restricted to the slopes above Clarence Drive between Gordon's Bay and Kogel Bay. Increasing threats include frequent fires, alien plants and urban development.

It is one of many species honouring the businessman and botanist Harry Bolus (1834–1911), who founded a chair of botany at the University of Cape Town and bequeathed to the university his fine herbarium and library.

S4 St4 O   Sep–Dec

Leucospermum rodolentum
Sandveld pincushion, Sandveldluisiesbos

Erect or spreading shrub to 3m, with densely grey-velvety, elliptical to wedge-shaped leaves 40–65mm long, tipped with 3–6 hard teeth; bearing clusters of up to 4 globular flowerheads 30–35mm in diameter at the branch tips, bright yellow; the style is usually straight and 15–25mm long. **HABITAT:** Sandy flats and lower slopes in southern Namaqualand and the southwestern Cape. **SIMILAR:** *Leucospermum tomentosum*, the Saldanha pincushion, from the West Coast, is a resprouting shrub to 1m with narrow, channelled leaves tipped with 1–3 hard teeth.

Sandveld pincushion is still relatively common on sandy flats around Hopefield but has lost almost half of its original range to agriculture and the extraction of groundwater.

Aug–Nov   S4 St4 <u>O</u>

Leucospermum hypophyllocarpodendron
Snake-stem pincushion

Sprawling to creeping shrublet with trailing stems and hairless or grey-felted, narrow and channelled to lance-shaped leaves all pointing vertically from the upper side of the stem, 40–130mm long and tipped with 2–4 hard teeth; bearing up to 4 rounded, slightly flattened flowerheads 30–40mm in diameter at the branch tips, bright yellow and sweetly scented; the style is straight or slightly curved inwards and 20–26mm long. **HABITAT:** Sandy coastal flats in the southwestern Cape.

The ungainly species epithet translates to 'beneath-the-foliage fruit tree', a reference to the characteristic habit in which the leaves project above the creeping stems and flower clusters.

Aug–Jan   S4 St4 <u>O</u>

Leucospermum conocarpodendron
Tree pincushion, Kreupelhout

Rounded shrub or tree to 5m with densely hairy branches and almost hairless or felted, elliptical to wedge-shaped leaves 60–115mm long, tipped with 3–10 hard teeth; bearing up to 3 globular to rounded flowerheads 70–90mm in diameter at branch tips, bright yellow; the style is slightly curved and 45–55mm long. **HABITAT:** Dry rocky slopes in extreme southwestern Cape.

The largest of the pincushions. The flowerheads are attractive but the short, crooked branches limit their value as cut flowers. The Afrikaans name, *Kreupelhout* translates to cripplewood. An alternative name, *Brandhout,* refers to its use for firewood in earlier times. The thick bark was used in tanning and huge numbers of trees were felled. The flowerheads are pollinated mainly by sugarbirds.

S4 St4 <u>O</u>   Aug–Dec

Leucospermum cordifolium
Pincushion, Bobbejaanklou

Rounded shrub with drooping branches to 1.5m and almost hairless, oval leaves 20–80mm long that are lobed at the base and tipped with 1–6 hard teeth; bearing up to 3 rounded, slightly flattened flowerheads 100–120mm in diameter at the branch tips, at right angles to the stem, orange to scarlet, with hairless floral tubes; the style is spreading to incurved and 45–60mm long. **HABITAT:** Rocky sandstone slopes in extreme southwestern Cape.

This is the iconic pincushion and one of the most important parents of hybrids and cultivars in flower markets around the world. The hard seeds are collected by ants, which carry them into their underground nests to remove the edible fleshy covering. Here they remain safe from predation until stimulated to germinate by a fire.

S4 St4 <u>O</u>   Aug–Jan

Leucospermum catherinae
Catherine-wheel pincushion, Wielblom

Shrub to 3m, with hairless, elliptical leaves, 90–135mm long, tipped with 3 or 4 hard teeth; bearing solitary, rounded, slightly flattened flowerheads ±150mm in diameter at the branch tips, orange to coppery bronze; the style is flexed and twisted clockwise near the tip and 70–80mm long. **HABITAT:** Sandstone slopes along streams in the interior mountains of the West Coast.

The specfic epithet honours local resident Catherine van der Byl, who was instrumental in making the species known to science, but it also has a more unpleasant connotation with the breaking wheel used for the martyrdom of Saint Catherine of Alexandria, early in the 4th century, by Emperor Maxentius.

Sep–Dec   S4 St4 <u>O</u>

Euchaetis longibracteata
Long-bracted euchaetis

Shrublet to 80cm with gland-dotted, oval to lance-shaped leaves ±10mm long, the uppermost leaves elongated into whitish, petal-like bracts that form a conspicuous collar around tight clusters of small pink flowers, each ornamented with minute, beard-like tufts of hairs at the mouth, with the narrow, stalk-like bases of the petals forming an erect cage around the short-styled ovary. **HABITAT:** Limestone hills on the Agulhas Plain.

A distinctive species easily recognised by the enlarged upper leaves, forming a collar of pale green false petals around the flowers. Other *Euchaetis* species lack this collar, but all members of the genus are characterised by the development of tufts of hairs at the base of each petal blade, blocking the mouth of the flowers.

Dec–Apr   S5 P5 St5 <u>O</u>

Phylica pubescens
Featherhead, Veerkoppie

 Shrub to 1.5m, with narrow leaves 25–35mm long with the margins rolled under; bearing minute, cup-shaped flowers in large, flattened heads surrounded by many leaves, and elongate, golden-silky bracts; the sepals are awn-like and the petals are minute and scale-like.
HABITAT: Sandstone and limestone slopes in the southwestern Cape.

Featherhead is popular in posies and in fresh and dried flower arrangements. It is also an excellent filler plant in gardens, offering a brilliant colour contrast to more conventional horticultural subjects, especially when the sunlight shimmers through the flowerheads.

S5 P5 St5 Ō   May–Aug

Berzelia lanuginosa
Kolkol, Vleiknoppiesbos

 Willowy shrub, 1.5–2m, with spreading to ascending, thread-like leaves less than 0.5mm wide, with black tips; bearing small, cream-coloured flowers in globular heads 5–8mm in diameter, arranged in short racemes and clustered terminally in loose groups. **HABITAT:** Damp sandstone slopes, seeps and streambanks.

A useful and attractive plant for seepage areas in gardens. Leafing and flowering shoots are marketed in the cut flower trade as 'Cape greens', and the vernacular name alludes to the appearance of the plants, visible from a distance as distinct patches (*kolle*) of bright green and white against the hillsides.

S5 P5 St5 Ō   Jun–Dec

Brunia laevis
Silver brunia, Vaalstompie

Rounded shrub to 1.5m, coppicing from a woody rootstock, with ascending, silvery grey, oblong leaves 3–5mm long that are incurved at the ends, with black tips and covered with minute hairs on the upper surface; bearing small white or cream-coloured flowers in globular heads 15–20mm in diameter, arranged in loose clusters. **HABITAT:** Rocky sandstone and limestone slopes in the extreme southwestern Cape.

Widely sold around the world as a component of festive bouquets, with an estimated 4.2 million stems exported annually. Poaching of stems is a threat to the formal wild flower industry. The Afrikaans name *stompie*, also applied to *Mimetes*, refers to the stumps that remain after the woody shrubs have been burned down in periodic wildfires.

Aug–Feb   S5 P5 St5 Ō

Brunia noduliflora
Common brunia, Knoppies, Volstruisies

Rounded shrub to 1.5m, coppicing from a woody rootstock, with minutely hairy branches and overlapping, triangular or lance-shaped leaves 2–3mm long pressed to the stem, with black tips; bearing small white flowers in globular heads ±10mm in diameter, arranged in loose clusters. **HABITAT:** Rocky sandstone slopes in the southwestern and southern Cape.

The Afrikaans vernacular name *Volstruisies* alludes to the fancied resemblance of the flowerheads to a brood of ostrich chicks. The branches are used as a long-lasting filler in flower arrangements.

Mar–Jul   S5 P5 St5 Ō

S5 P5 St5 Ō   Jun–Feb

Staavia radiata
Glass-eyes, Glasogies, Altydbos

 Rounded, twiggy shrublet to 60cm, coppicing from a woody rootstock, with ascending, narrowly lance-shaped leaves 4–10mm long, with black tips; bearing small pink flowers in heads ±5mm in diameter, surrounded by a whorl of spreading white bracts. **HABITAT:** Sandy flats near the coast in the southwestern Cape.

The cut branches are used as a long-lasting filler in flower arrangements.

P5 St5 Ō   Oct–May

Helichrysum foetidum
Skunkleaf everlasting, Muishondblaar

 Robust biennial herb to 1m, covered with gland-tipped hairs producing a foetid odour, with oblong to lance-shaped leaves clasping the stem and with ear-shaped lobes on each side at the base, rough-haired above and grey-woolly beneath; bearing leafy clusters of flattened globular flowerheads 15–25mm in diameter, with a central button of deep yellow florets surrounded by several series of dry-papery, pale yellowish bracts. The fruits are topped with barbed bristles enabling them to drift on the wind. **HABITAT:** Damp rocky slopes from southwestern to Eastern Cape, especially after fire, then disappearing until seeds germinate by disturbance or fire.

Traditionally used for medical and magical purposes. The leaves are said to be antibiotic.

Syncarpha canescens

Pink everlasting, Pienksewejaartjie

Sparsely branched shrublet to 50cm, with small, elliptical leaves that are grey-felted on both surfaces; bearing solitary or loosely clustered, top-shaped flowerheads 25–35mm in diameter, with a central button of purplish, funnel-shaped florets surrounded and overtopped by several overlapping rows of dry-papery, sharply pointed, glossy pink to red bracts that are the most showy part of the heads. The fruits are topped with small, feathery bristles that enable them to drift on the wind. **HABITAT:** Drier rocky sandstone slopes and flats throughout the southwestern and southern Cape.

The cut stems dry very well. They make an attractive addition to dried flower arrangements.

Jan–Sep   P5 St5 Ō

Syncarpha vestita

Cape snow, White everlasting

Compact, softly woody shrublet to 1m, with paddle-shaped leaves that are grey-woolly on both surfaces; bearing solitary or loosely clustered, top-shaped flowerheads 35–40mm in diameter, often nested in the upper leaves, with a central button of purple, funnel-shaped florets surrounded and overtopped by several overlapping rows of dry-papery, sharply pointed, glossy white bracts. The fruits are topped with small, feathery bristles that enable them to drift on the wind. **HABITAT:** Rocky slopes and flats in the southwestern and southern Cape, thriving in the years after a fire.

The papery bracts open properly only on warm, sunny days. The flowerheads are sometimes garishly dyed for use in dried flower arrangements.

Nov–Jan   P5 St5 Ō

Syncarpha speciosissima
Cape everlasting

 Sprawling shrublet with erect annual stems 20–60cm, and oblong to linear leaves clasping the stem at the base and white-woolly on both surfaces; bearing solitary, hemispherical flowerheads 30–40mm in diameter, on elongate peduncles, with a central button of yellow, funnel-shaped florets surrounded and overtopped by several overlapping rows of dry-papery, sharply pointed, glossy, ivory-coloured bracts that are the most showy part of the heads. The fruits are topped with small, feathery bristles that enable them to drift on the wind. **HABITAT:** Sandstone slopes in the southwestern Cape.

The cut stems dry very well and are an attractive addition to dried flower arrangements.

P5 St5 Ō　　Jul–Jan

Edmondia sesamoides
Scale-leaved everlasting

 Slender-stemmed shrublet to 30cm, with erect, overlapping leaves that are more or less differentiated into 2 kinds: those on the lower and vegetative branches are needle-like with the margins rolled upwards, and those on the flowering stalks are scale-like; bearing solitary, top-shaped flowerheads 25–30mm in diameter, with a central button of yellow or purplish, funnel-shaped florets surrounded and overtopped by several overlapping rows of dry-papery, sharply pointed, glossy white to pink or creamy yellow bracts that are the most showy part of the heads. The fruits are topped with small, feathery bristles that enable them to drift on the wind. **HABITAT:** Rocky flats and slopes in the southwestern and southern Cape.

The cut stems dry very well and are an attractive addition to dried flower arrangements.

P5 St5 Ō　　Aug–Dec

Phaenocoma prolifera
Coral-reef everlasting, Rooisewejaartjie

Stiffly branched shrublet with white-woolly stems to 60cm, with overlapping, granular leaves on short shoots that branch from stems at right angles; bearing solitary, large, top-shaped flowerheads 30–40mm in diameter, with central button of purplish florets, outer ones thread-like and inner ones funnel-shaped, surrounded by series of dry-papery, glossy pink to red bracts. Fruits are topped with small, feathery bristles that enable them to drift on wind. **HABITAT:** Sandstone slopes in fynbos in the southwestern and southern Cape.

The bracts have a complex and characteristic structure, each divided into a lower shaft, a central hinge, and an upper blade, enabling them to open on sunny days and close in inclement or wet weather.

| Sep–Mar | P5 St5 Ō |

Metalasia muricata
Bristlebush, Blombos

Shrub to 2.5m or more, with small, needle-like to lance-shaped leaves 2–15mm long, twisted and often flexed downwards, with hooked tips and with margins rolled upwards and woolly in the groove thus formed; bearing flat-topped clusters of small, cylindrical flowerheads at the branch tips, each containing 3–5 small florets surrounded by a series of dry, scale-like bracts, the uppermost white and petal-like. The fruits are topped with small, feathery bristles. **HABITAT:** Coastal sands from southwestern Cape to southern KwaZulu-Natal.

Blombos Cave, named for the shrub, is a famous archaeological site near Mossel Bay that was occupied during the Middle and Late Stone Ages. Among the most important finds at the cave is an etched ochre fragment interpreted as the earliest drawing by a human.

| May–Sep | P5 St5 Ō |

P5 St5 Ō   Oct–Nov

Corymbium africanum
Rough-leaved corymbium, Plampers

Tufted perennial with rough-haired stems to 30cm, and thread- to strap-like leaves clustered at the bottom of the stem and silky at the base; bearing flat-topped clusters of small, spindle-shaped flowerheads, each containing a solitary, funnel-shaped, purple, pink or white floret surrounded by 2 series of sticky, rough-haired bracts. **HABITAT:** Sandy flats and slopes in the southwestern and Eastern Cape.

The growth form of the plants is distinctive, resembling some wild iris rather than a daisy. Flowering is stimulated by fire and plants are seldom seen at other times. The origin of the Afrikaans name may derive from the Dutch *pluimpje* or plume, for the resemblance of the flower clusters to the clipped feathers or hackle worn on some regimental headgear.

P5 St5 Ō   Sep–May

Gerbera crocea
Cape gerbera, Dialstee

Tufted perennial herb to 40cm, with a rosette of stalked, lance-shaped to elliptical leaves that are hairless to sparsely cobwebby beneath, their margins lightly toothed and rolled under; bearing solitary white or pink, daisy-like flowerheads on long, scaly stems, with a white or pink central disc and the rays maroon beneath; each head is cupped by several series of pointed, hairless to sparsely cobwebby bracts. The fruits are topped with stiff bristles. **HABITAT:** Sandstone slopes in the southwestern Cape, flowering after fire.

The florists' gerberas are hybrids and selections of species from eastern South Africa, readily distinguished from the fynbos species by their naked flower stalks lacking scale-like bracts.

Gerbera linnaei
Fern-leaved gerbera, Varingblom

Tufted perennial to 40cm, with a rosette of narrow leaves that are cut into round, twisted lobes with the margins rolled under, and yellowish-felted beneath; bearing solitary white or cream-coloured or rarely pink daisy-like flowerheads on long, scaly stems, with a dark-tinged central disc eye and the rays maroon beneath; each head is cupped by several series of pointed, hairless bracts. The fruits are topped with stiff bristles.
HABITAT: Sandstone slopes in the exteme southwestern Cape, flowering after fire.

The closely lobed leaves are very distinctive. Fern-leaved gerbera hybridises with Cape gerbera where the two species grow together.

Oct–Jan   P5 St5 O̅

Cullumia squarrosa
Leafy snakethistle, Steekhaarbos

Sprawling, densely leafy shrublet to 50cm, cobwebby on the young parts, with spreading or arched, sharply needle-like leaves mostly 15–25mm long with spiny bristly margins that are rolled under; bearing solitary yellow, daisy-like flowerheads nested in the upper leaves at the branch tips; each head is cupped by 4 series of spiny bracts with the upper row lacking prickles. The fruits are smooth and elliptical, like grains of rice.
HABITAT: Coastal bush in the extreme southwestern Cape.

Snakethistles are closely related to yellowthistles, from which they differ in their smooth, grain-like fruits. All of the species are found in fynbos.

Sep–Dec   P5 St5 O̅

Berkheya armata
Cape Flats yellowthistle, Vlaktedissel

Tufted perennial to 40cm, with a basal rosette of lance-shaped leaves, hairless above and white-felted beneath, with prickly-toothed margins that are slightly rolled under; bearing 1 to a few yellow, sunflower-like flowerheads on a leafy stem; each head is cupped by several series of finely prickly bracts. The fruits are topped with a crown of scales. **HABITAT:** Clay and granite slopes and flats in the southwestern Cape.

An attractive species with large flowerheads, favouring richer granite or clay soils.

P5 St5 $\bar{0}$ Sep–Nov

Berkheya herbacea
Herbaceous yellowthistle, Kaaldissel

Tufted perennial to 40cm, with a basal rosette of lance-shaped leaves, hairless above and white-felted beneath, with scarcely prickly-toothed margins; bearing several yellow, sunflower-like flowerheads on a leafy stem; each head is cupped by several series of bracts, the lower/outer ones prickly but the inner/upper ones with broad, smooth, horny margins. The fruits are topped with a crown of scales. **HABITAT:** Sandstone slopes in the southwestern Cape. Flowering best after fire.

The smooth, horny margins of the floral bracts are distinctive: other yellowthistles have floral bracts with prickly or spiny margins.

P5 St5 0   Oct–Mar

Berkheya barbata
Opposite-leaved yellowthistle

White-felted shrublet to 60cm, sprouting from a woody rootstock, with opposite pairs of elliptical leaves, smooth above when mature but persistently white-felted beneath, with prickly-toothed margins that are rolled under; bearing solitary, yellow, sunflower-like flowerheads on white-felted stalks; each head is cupped by several series of very prickly bracts. The fruits are topped with a crown of scales. **HABITAT:** Rocky sandstone slopes in the southwestern Cape.

A striking species that is especially conspicuous after a veld fire. The leaves in opposite pairs are characteristic.

Aug–Dec   P5 St5 Ō

Gazania krebsiana
Common gazania

Tufted perennial to 20cm, with a basal tuft of variable leaves, either undivided or divided into narrow segments, with the margins rolled under, white-felted beneath and exuding a milky latex when damaged; bearing solitary yellow to orange or reddish daisy-like flowerheads on hollow, leafless stalks, with a dark centre and often with dark marks at the base of the rays; each head is cupped by a hairless or thinly hairy, toothed collar. **HABITAT:** Roadsides, flats and lower slopes throughout southern Africa to Tanzania.

Gazanias are excellent colonisers of lightly disturbed soils and are palatable to many stock animals. Common gazania is a popular garden plant and has contributed to the numerous horticultural forms available in the nursery trade.

Aug–Jan   P5 St5 Ō

P5 St5 O̅   Aug–Oct

Arctotis hirsuta

West Coast arctotis, Weskusgousblom

Slightly fleshy, often robust, annual herb to 45cm, with sparsely hairy, lyre-shaped, divided leaves, often with ear-like lobes at the base; bearing yellow, cream or orange daisy-like flowerheads on hollow stems, with a black disc or eye; each flowerhead is cupped by 5 or 6 series of bracts, the outer ones with short, hairy tails and the inner ones with broad, membranous tips. The small, black fruits have a pair of rounded cavities on 1 side and a crown of small scales at the top. **HABITAT:** Sandy slopes and flats, usually coastal, in the southwestern Cape.

A beautiful annual for gardens. It is still readily seen in and around the West Coast National Park.

P5 St5 O̅   Aug–Oct

Arctotis acaulis

Tufted arctotis, Renostergousblom

Tufted perennial to 20cm, with a basal rosette of lance- to lyre-shaped, toothed leaves that are roughly hairy above and grey-felted beneath; bearing solitary orange, yellow or cream daisy-like flowerheads on hollow, hairy, leafless stalks, with a black disc or eye; each flowerhead is cupped by 5 or 6 series of bracts, the outer ones with slender, woolly tails and the inner ones with broad, membranous tips. The fruits have a pair of rounded cavities and are topped with several large, papery scales. **HABITAT:** Clay, granitic, and limestone flats in the southwestern and southern Cape.

An excellent garden plant for sunny places, best treated as an annual.

Arctotis stoechadifolia
Silver arctotis, Silwergousblom

Sprawling, silvery-woolly perennial with erect shoots to 35cm, and white-felted, lance-shaped to lobed leaves; bearing solitary, cream-coloured daisy-like flowerheads on hollow, woolly, leafless stalks with rays reddish on reverse and a black disc or eye; each flowerhead is cupped by 5 or 6 series of bracts, the outer ones with woolly tails and the inner ones with broad, membranous tips. Fruits have a pair of elongated cavities and are topped with large, papery scales. **HABITAT:** Dunes and sandy flats, mostly coastal, from Table Bay to Langebaan.

This tough, beautiful species can form large mats along roadsides and on dunes but occurs naturally only along a small stretch of coast from Table Bay to Langebaan, where it is increasingly threatened by development.

Sep–Dec   P5 St5 Ō

Arctotheca calendula
Cape-dandelion, Cape weed

Tufted or sprawling annual herb to 20cm, with mostly basal leaves that are scalloped to deeply divided, and roughly hairy above but white-woolly beneath; bearing solitary, pale to deep yellow daisy-like flowerheads on hollow, roughly hairy, leafless stalks, the heads with a black disc often surrounded by a paler halo; each flowerhead is cupped by 5 or 6 series of bracts with broad, membranous margins and tips. Fruits are woolly with a tuft of small, chaffy scales at the top. **HABITAT:** Coastal areas or disturbed soil from Namaqualand to Eastern Cape, often forming dense stands in fallow lands on sandy soil.

Both the annual Cape-dandelion and the creeping perennial species, *Arctotheca prostrata*, are recorded as noxious invasives in Australia and California.

Jun–Nov   P5 St5 Ō

Ursinia anthemoides
Dull-eyed parachute-daisy, Magriet

 Annual herb to 50cm, with leaves 20–50mm long, once- or twice-divided into thread-like segments; bearing solitary yellow or orange daisy-like flowerheads 15–60mm in diameter on slender stems, with a dull, black disc or eye and the rays sometimes darker at the base and on the reverse; each flowerhead is cupped with several series of bracts, the outer ones triangular with black edges and the inner ones tipped with a broad, papery flap. The fruits are topped with 5 white, papery, petal-like scales. **HABITAT:** Sandy and gravel slopes and flats from southern Namibia to the Eastern Cape.

A pretty annual species for sunny gardens. The fruits, topped with five papery white scales, resemble small flowers.

P5 St5 Ō   Aug–Oct

Ursinia paleacea
Showy parachute-daisy, Geelmagriet

 Shrub to 90cm, with leaves 20–60mm long that are finely divided into thread-like segments; bearing solitary yellow or brownish daisy-like flowerheads 20–50mm in diameter on long, slender stems, with a yellow disc or eye and the rays sometimes greenish at the base and dark on the reverse; each flowerhead is cupped with several series of bracts, the outer ones triangular with black edges and the inner ones tipped with a broad, papery flap. The fruits are topped with 5 white, papery, petal-like scales. **HABITAT:** Sandstone and granite slopes in the southwestern and southern Cape, especially after fire.

Parachute-daisies are allied to Chamomile. A brandy tincture of *Ursinia abrotanifolia* was an early Cape medicine.

P5 St5 Ō   Aug–Dec

Senecio littoreus
West Coast groundsel, Geelhongerblom

Almost hairless or short-haired annual herb to 40cm, with toothed to shallowly lobed, oblong to lance-shaped leaves, and a stem that is loosely branched above, bearing yellow daisy-like flowerheads 15–20mm in diameter; each flowerhead is held by a cylindrical cup formed by a single series of narrow, green bracts cohering along their margins, with additional minute scales at the base. The slender fruits are topped with fine white bristles. **HABITAT:** Mainly found on coastal sands in southern Namaqualand and the southwestern Cape. **SIMILAR:** *Senecio abruptus* is similar but has more deeply lobed leaves.

West Coast groundsel has great potential as a garden plant but is scarcely known in cultivation.

Aug–Nov   P5 St5 Ō

Senecio arenarius
Purple groundsel, Hongerblom

Sticky annual herb, 15–40cm, covered in gland-tipped hairs, with toothed or lobed leaves, the margins sometimes rolled under, and a stem that is loosely branched above, bearing daisy-like flowerheads 20–30mm in diameter, with mauve or white rays and a yellow disc; each flowerhead is held by a cylindrical cup formed by a single series of narrow, sticky, green bracts cohering along their margins, with a few additional minute scales at the base. The slender fruits are topped with fine white bristles. **HABITAT:** Sandy flats from southern Namibia to the southwestern Cape.

The Afrikaans vernacular name *Hongerblom* ('hungerflower') derives from the purported use of certain species as a tea to promote the appetite.

Jul–Sep   P5 St5 Ō

P5 St5 Ō   Sep–Nov

Senecio elegans
Veld-cineraria

Sticky, annual herb to 1m, densely covered in gland-tipped hairs, with fleshy, deeply lobed or divided leaves, the margins rolled under, and a stem that is loosely branched above, bearing daisy-like flowerheads 20–30mm in diameter, with mauve or white rays and a yellow disc; each flowerhead is held by a rounded cup formed by a single series of narrow green bracts cohering along their margins, with many additional smaller, black-tipped scales at the base. The slender fruits are topped with fine white bristles. **HABITAT:** Coastal sands from the southwestern to the Eastern Cape.

A rewarding and showy annual for sandy and coastal gardens.

P5 St5 Ō   Sep–Dec

Senecio umbellatus
Thread-leaved purple ragwort

Wand-like perennial to 80cm, hairless or sometimes sparsely hairy below, with narrow, thread-like leaves, or these divided into thread-like lobes, with the margins rolled under and minutely toothed; bearing loosely branched clusters of daisy-like flowerheads 20–30mm in diameter, with magenta to pink or sometimes white rays and a yellow disc; each flowerhead is held by a cylindrical cup formed by a single series of narrow green bracts cohering along their margins, with additional minute scales at the base. The slender fruits are topped with fine white bristles. **HABITAT:** Moist sandstone flats and slopes in the southwestern and southern Cape. **SIMILAR:** *Senecio paniculatus* has disc-like flowerheads.

An attractive species that is especially evident in moist places after a veld fire.

Senecio burchellii
Molteno disease plant, Geelgifbossie

 Softly woody shrublet to 40cm, mostly hairless but sometimes roughly hairy below, with narrow leaves that have margins rolled under and are sometimes sparsely toothed, usually with axillary tufts of smaller leaves; bearing loose clusters of yellow daisy-like flowerheads 10mm in diameter; each held by a cylindrical cup formed by many narrow green bracts cohering along their margins, with additional minute scales at the base. The slender fruits are topped with fine, white bristles; the involucre is conical. **HABITAT:** Sandy and stony slopes from Namibia to the Eastern Cape.

Senecio burchellii is one of many species containing toxic alkaloids responsible for stock losses. Even small quantitites of *Senecio* can cause liver damage.

Jan–Dec   P5 St5 Ō

Senecio halimifolius
Tobaccobush, Tabakbos

 Greyish shrub to 1.5m, with sparsely white-cobwebby, lance-shaped leaves that are broader and coarsely toothed above; bearing dense clusters of small yellow daisy-like flowerheads 8–10mm in diameter; each flowerhead held by a cylindrical cup formed by a single series of many narrow green bracts cohering along their margins, with additional minute scales at the base. The slender fruits are topped with fine white bristles. **HABITAT:** Coastal sands in damp places along seeps or lagoons in the southwestern Cape.

Tobaccobush has been shown to be toxic to animals. The common name refers to the resemblance of its leaves to those of Tree tobacco, *Nictotiana glauca*, and not to their use.

Nov–Jan   P5 St5 Ō

P5 St5 Ō   Nov–Jan

Senecio rigidus
Rough ragwort

 Densely leafy shrub with coarsely hairy stems to 1.5m, and oblong to rounded, rough-haired, irregularly toothed leaves with the margins rolled under, often woolly beneath with raised veins; bearing branched clusters of small, yellow daisy-like flowerheads 8–10mm; each flowerhead held by a cylindrical cup formed by a single series of many narrow green bracts cohering along their margins, with additional minute scales at the base. The slender fruits are topped with fine white bristles. **HABITAT:** Sandstone slopes and gullies in the southwestern and southern Cape, germinating especially after fire.

Rough ragwort is especially common in moist gullies on mountain slopes after fire, sometimes forming dense stands.

P5 St5 Ō   Jul–Nov

Othonna parviflora
Giant babooncress, Bobbejaankool

 Robust shrub to 2m, single-stemmed at the base and branching above, with hairless, leathery, lance-shaped leaves with smooth or finely toothed margins; bearing dense, flat-topped, branched clusters of numerous small, yellow daisy-like flowerheads 5–8mm in diameter; each flowerhead held by a cylindrical cup formed by a single series of smooth, oblong green bracts cohering along their margins. The silky fruits are topped with fine beige bristles; they are formed only by the outer ring of ray florets. **HABITAT:** Sandstone slopes in the mountains of the southwestern and southern Cape.

Common along several of the mountain passes in the southwestern and southern Cape, notably Bainskloof, Michell's and Pakhuis passes.

Euryops speciosissimus
Giant resinbush, Pronkharpuisbos

 Slender, single-stemmed shrub to over 2m, with a white waxy covering on the young parts, with leaves 60–200mm long clustered at the branch tips, deeply divided into flexible, thread-like lobes; bearing solitary, large, yellow daisy-like flowerheads ±70mm in diameter on stout, naked stalks; each flowerhead held by a single series of smooth, green bracts joined at the base into a cup. The fruits are topped with a few short bristles that soon fall off. **HABITAT:** Rocky sandstone slopes in the interior mountains along the West Coast. **SIMILAR:** Several similar species differ in the length of their leaves and the lobing.

A striking and sculptural species that deserves to be seen more in cultivation. The dried fruiting stalks are sometimes used in floral arrangements.

Aug–Nov   P5 St5 O̅

Euryops abrotanifolius
Mountain resinbush, Bergharpuisbos

 Densely leafy shrub to 1m, with leaves 60–90mm long, deeply divided into thread-like or needle-like lobes; bearing solitary yellow daisy-like flowerheads on naked stalks that are woolly at the base; each flowerhead held by a single series of smooth, green bracts joined at the base into a cup. The smooth, closely ribbed fruits are topped with a fleshy appendage, and a few short bristles that soon fall off. **HABITAT:** Sandstone slopes in the southwestern and southern Cape.

Especially common on the lower slopes of Table Mountain and Lion's Head on the Cape Peninsula. The resinous gum of various resinbush species was used medicinally by early colonists.

Jul–Dec   P5 St5 O̅

P5 St5 Ō   Mar–Sep

Osteospermum moniliferum
Tickberry, Bosluisbessie, Bietou

Rounded shrub to over 1.5m, sparsely woolly on the young parts, with oval to elliptical, toothed leaves; bearing small clusters of yellow daisy-like flowerheads ± 20mm in diameter; each flowerhead cupped by 2–4 rows of hairless or sparsely woolly bracts. Fruits are fleshy and green, turning glossy black when ripe, 6–8mm long; they are formed only by the outer ring of ray florets. **HABITAT:** Sandstone and limestone slopes and flats from Namaqualand to tropical Africa. **SIMILAR:** Grey tickberry, *Osteospermum incanum*, is a sprawling, often grey-woolly shrublet with thorny branches.

An asset to coastal gardens and still widely known under the name *Chrysanthemoides*. The berries attract fruit-eating birds and were harvested by the Khoisan as a food source. *Bietou* is one of the few Khoi names still in use.

P5 St5 Ō   Aug–Oct

Osteospermum monstrosum
Dark-eyed windowseed, Trekkertjie

Foetid, annual herb to 40cm, covered with gland-tipped hairs, the stem branching above, with fleshy, lance-shaped, toothed to lobed leaves clustered towards the base; bearing branched clusters of daisy-like flowerheads 15–20mm in diameter, with pale yellow rays, often brownish at the base, and a dark purplish disc or eye; each flowerhead cupped by 2–4 rows of glandular bracts. The fruits are 8–9mm long, with 3 papery wings down the sides and a solitary translucent window at the top; they are formed only by the outer ring of ray florets. **HABITAT:** Sandy and rocky flats from southern Namibia to the southwestern Cape.

This annual species was long known as *Tripteris clandestinum*. It is a weed in Western Australia under the name, Stinking Roger.

Dimorphotheca pluvialis
Rain-daisy, Reënblommetjie

 Erect to sprawling annual herb to 30cm, branching from the base and covered in gland-tipped hairs, with lance-shaped, lobed to toothed leaves; bearing solitary, large daisy-like flowerheads 40–60mm in diameter at the branch tips, with white rays that are sometimes purple at the base and darker on the reverse, and a black disc or eye; each flowerhead cupped by 2–4 rows of rough-haired bracts. **HABITAT:** Sandy and clay flats and slopes from southern Namibia to southern Cape.

The flowerheads open mid-morning on warm, sunny days. Each head produces two kinds of seeds: small, warty outer ones with a hard coat, which remain dormant for extended periods, and disc-shaped inner ones that are readily dispersed by wind and can germinate immediately.

Aug–Oct   P5 St5 O̅

Oncosiphon suffruticosum
Stinkweed, Stinkkruid

 Aromatic annual herb to 50cm, much-branched above, with finely twice- to thrice-divided leaves; bearing flat-topped clusters of dull yellow, button-like flowerheads 5–8mm in diameter containing small 4-lobed florets; each flowerhead cupped by several rows of small bracts with narrow membranous margins. The small, flask-shaped fruits are 4-ribbed and topped with small, irregular scales. **HABITAT:** Sandy flats and slopes, often coastal in waste ground, from southern Namibia to the West Coast. **SIMILAR:** Greater stinkweed, *Oncosiphon grandiflorum*, has larger flowerheads 8–10mm in diameter.

Stinkweed, a relative of Chamomile, was traditionally used as an antispasmodic for stomach ailments. Dried plants were burned as a household fumigant.

Sep–Dec   P4 St5 O̅

Cotula turbinata
Gooseweed, Ganskos

Delicate, softly hairy, annual herb, 5–30cm, with finely twice- or thrice-divided leaves; bearing small, white, short-rayed flowerheads 8–12mm in diameter on wiry, leafless stalks that become inflated or swollen at the tip like a top when in fruit, the heads containing 4-lobed florets; each flowerhead is cupped by 2 rows of rounded, 3-veined bracts. The fruits are small and elliptical. **HABITAT:** Sandy or disturbed places in the southwestern Cape, often in waste ground. **SIMILAR:** Often growing with Yellow gooseweed, *Cotula pruinosa*, with bright yellow flowerheads.

Gooseweed is common on road verges and waste ground around Cape Town. The vernacular name derives from its palatability to geese.

P4 St5 Ō — Jun–Oct

Heterolepis aliena
Rock-daisy

Sprawling, closely leafy shrublet to 30cm from a woody rootstock, with cobwebby branches and stiff, needle-like leaves (10) 15–30mm long, that are densely woolly beneath with the margins rolled under and sparsely toothed; bearing solitary yellow daisy-like flowerheads 40–50mm in diameter on short, roughly hairy peduncles to 50mm long at the branch tips; each flowerhead is cupped by 2 or 3 rows of green bracts with membranous margins, but the inner bracts are almost entirely membranous. Fruits flask-shaped, densely silky, topped with 2 unequal rows of stout, tawny, barbed bristles. **HABITAT:** Rocky sandstone slopes and outcrops in the mountains of the southwestern Cape.

Flowering plants make a bold splash of colour against the rocks during early summer, their roots protected from the direct sun in cracks or beneath boulders.

P5 St5 Ō — Sep–Jan

Leysera gnaphalodes
Yellow tea-daisy, Geeltee

Slender, almost hairless to cobwebby shrublet or short-lived perennial herb to 40cm, with needle-like leaves covered in gland-tipped hairs; bearing solitary yellow daisy-like flowerheads 10–15mm in diameter on slender, wiry stalks; each flowerhead is cupped by several rows of firm, glandular-haired bracts. The slender fruits are topped with feathery bristles. **HABITAT:** Dry, sandy and stony flats and slopes from southern Namibia to the Eastern Cape.

An infusion of the dried leaves was used as an emollient to treat coughs.

Sep–Jan   P5 St5 O̅

Athanasia trifurcata
Colterbush, Klaaslouwbos, Kouterbos

Single-stemmed shrublet to 1.5m, with more or less upright, hairless to scurfy, wedge-shaped grey leaves that are 3–5-toothed at the tips; bearing tight, flat-topped clusters of broadly cylindrical, yellow, button-like flowerheads containing 50–100 florets each; the flowerheads are cupped by 3–5 rows of chaffy bracts. The fruits are ribbed and topped with a crown of stalked glands. **HABITAT:** Flats and rocky slopes from Namaqualand to the Eastern Cape, in disturbed ground, along roadsides and especially in overused lands.

The Afrikaans vernacular name *Kouterbos* derives from the propensity of the plants, which can occur in dense stands in old lands, for packing up against the colter (*kouter*) of the plough. Heavy infestations were a sign of degraded lands and looming bankruptcy.

Sep–Dec   P5 St5 O̅

P5 St5 Ō   Nov–Dec

Hymenolepis crithmifolia
False karoo, Basterkaroo

Upright shrub to 3m, densely leafy at the branch tips, with large, leathery leaves that are finely divided into needle-like segments with the margins rolled under; bearing small, dull yellow, cylindrical flowerheads massed together in densely branched, flat-topped clusters; each flowerhead is cupped by 3–5 rows of chaffy bracts. The flask-shaped fruits are closely ribbed with a tuft of small fringed scales. **HABITAT:** Rocky sandstone slopes in Namaqualand and the southwestern Cape, often along roadsides.

A fine, quick-growing shrub for large, sunny gardens, producing masses of honey-scented blooms in early summer.

P5 St5 Ō   Jan–Nov

Eriocephalus africanus
Wild-rosemary, Kapokbossie

Twiggy shrub to 1m, with narrow, sometimes forked, silvery-silky leaves in opposite pairs with tufts of smaller leaves in the axils; bearing erect or arching sprays of small flowerheads on wiry stalks, crowded in flat-topped clusters at the branch tips, each head with a few wedge-shaped white rays and a small purple disc or eye; each flowerhead is cupped by 1 row of 4–6 rounded bracts. The fruits are densely woolly. **HABITAT:** Mostly clay or granite hillsides from southern Namaqualand to the Eastern Cape.

Brandy-based infusions of Wild-rosemary were used traditionally as a diuretic. Today the plant is an important source of essential oils for perfumes, and dried leaves can be used as a herb in cooking. The fluffy seeds are used as a nest lining by some birds.

Osmitopsis asteriscoides
Marsh balsam-daisy, Belskruie

 Aromatic, camphor-scented shrub with erect stems to 2m that are sparsely branched and densely leafy above, with ascending, overlapping, smooth or felted, lance-shaped leaves 10–60(80)mm long; bearing loose clusters of white daisy-like flowerheads with a yellow disc or eye; each flowerhead cupped by 2–4 rows of narrow, overlapping bracts. The fruits are smooth. **HABITAT:** Marshes and seeps on sandstone in the extreme southwestern Cape.

A brandy tincture (*belsbrandewyn*) of the leaves is a traditional remedy for chest and stomach complaints and was also used as a tonic and antiseptic.

Aug–Feb   P5 St5 Ō

Felicia aethiopica
Garden felicia, Bloublommetjie

 Sparsely hairy, soft-stemmed shrublet to 1m, with opposite pairs of elliptical to oval leaves that are often flexed downwards; bearing solitary, mauve to blue daisy-like flowerheads 15–20mm in diameter, on elongate, often reddish stalks, with a yellow disc or eye; each flowerhead is cupped by 2 series of narrow green bracts. The fruits are flattened and elliptical with a tuft of slender, white, barbed bristles. **HABITAT:** Rocky flats and slopes from the southwestern Cape to KwaZulu-Natal.

A very popular garden plant available in several colour selections; readily propogated from seeds and cuttings.

Jan–Dec   P5 St5 Ō

Felicia tenella
Dainty felicia

Sparsely hairy annual, 5–25cm, with narrow leaves that are coarsely bristly on the margins; bearing daisy-like flowerheads on slender stalks, with blue, violet or white rays and a yellow disc or eye; each flowerhead is cupped by 3 or 4 series of narrow green bracts. The fruits are flattened and elliptical with a tuft of slender, white, barbed bristles that readily drop off. **HABITAT:** Near water or on coastal dunes in the southwestern Cape.

One of several annual *Felicia* species that are still relatively common around Cape Town. The narrow leaves are distinctive.

P5 St5 Ō   Aug–Nov

Scabiosa africana
Cape scabious

Sprawling shrublet to 1m, with opposite pairs of soft-textured, velvety leaves that are toothed or cut along the margins; bearing small, lilac, asymmetrically funnel-shaped flowers in heads 30–45mm in diameter. The small fruits are topped with a papery, saucer-like collar and 5 whisker-like awns. **HABITAT:** Sheltered granite and sandstone slopes on the Cape Peninsula and southern Paardeberg.

An easily cultivated and showy perennial for gardens, producing long-lasting flowerheads that are attractive to butterflies and bees.

S5 P5 St4 Ō   Jul–Nov

Erica caffra
Water heath, Waterheide

 Erect shrub or small tree to 4m, with strong, twisted branches and spreading, needle-like leaves; bearing velvety, white or yellowish flowers 5–6mm long towards the end of the branches, conical in shape with small, spreading lobes and anthers hidden within the tube. **HABITAT:** Beside streams on flats and mountain slopes from the southwestern Cape to southern KwaZulu-Natal.

There are ±860 species of heath worldwide, distributed through Africa, Madagascar and Europe, with almost 80 per cent of the species confined to southern Africa. *Erica* is by far the largest genus in the fynbos, where it numbers some 660 species, accounting for over seven per cent of all fynbos species. Several species are cultivated and others are important in the cut flower trade.

Jul–Dec   S4 P4 St8 <u>O</u>

Erica hirtiflora
Pink mist

 Erect shrublet to 1m with small, needle-like leaves; bearing numerous hairy, mauve to pink flowers 3–4mm long towards the end of the branches, egg- or urn-shaped with a constricted mouth and anthers contained in the tube. **HABITAT:** Moist flats and slopes in seepages in the extreme southwestern Cape, forming dense stands on the Cape Peninsula.

Four-fifths of Cape ericas have small to moderate-sized pink flowers pollinated by insects, mainly bees, but also some specialised nectar-feeding flies. Another 15 per cent have larger, often bicoloured flowers, pollinated by sunbirds, and a minority, with insignificant flowers and large, protruding stigmas, are wind pollinated.

Jan–Dec   S4 P4 St8 <u>O</u>

Erica multumbellifera
Bead heath

 Erect shrublet to 40cm with small, needle-like leaves; bearing clusters of slightly sticky, purple to red, musty-scented flowers 4mm long, globular or bead-like in shape with a small mouth and small, erect lobes, the anthers hidden within the tube. **HABITAT:** Sandy flats and mountains in the southwestern Cape.

A pretty species easily seen in the nature reserves at Silvermine and Cape Point.

S4 P4 St8 <u>O</u>   Nov–Jun

Erica baccans
Berry heath

 Sturdy, somewhat willowy shrub to 3m, with small, needle-like leaves pressed to the surface. Bears hairless, rose pink flowers 5mm long in a small cluster at the tip of the branches, globular with indentations at the base and a narrow throat with small erect lobes, with prominent, keeled, rather dry, petal-like sepals giving the flowers a squared appearance, and crested anthers contained within the tube. **HABITAT:** Dense stands on mountainsides on the Cape Peninsula.

This species is responsible for the pink blush that mists the slopes of Table Mountain above Kirstenbosch each year.

S4 P4 St8 <u>O</u>   Apr–Aug

Erica coriifolia
Leathery-leaved heath

Erect shrublet to 1m, with small, needle-like leaves pressed to the surface; bearing hairless, pink flowers 3–10mm long in a cluster at the tip of the branches, urn-shaped with a narrow mouth, soon turning brown at the tips, with large, petal-like sepals almost covering the petals, and crested anthers hidden in the tube. **HABITAT:** Common on sandy flats and middle to upper slopes in the extreme southwestern Cape.

Jan–Dec   S4 P4 St8 <u>O</u>

Erica bruniades
Kapokkie

Erect shrublet to 50cm with soft-haired, small, needle-like leaves pressed to the surface; bearing small clusters of woolly flowers 3–4mm long, urn-shaped and completely covered in silvery, white or pink hairs, with brown stamens protruding from the small mouth. **HABITAT:** Sandy flats, lower slopes and plateaus in the southwestern Cape.

Aug–Dec   S4 P4 St8 <u>O</u>

Erica lutea
Rice heath, Geelrysheide

Erect shrublet to 90cm with lanky branches with small, needle-like leaves pressed to the surface; bearing hairless, yellow to white flowers 7–10mm long crowded towards the end of the branches, conical-tubular with star-like, spreading lobes, prominent petal-like sepals, and crested anthers hidden within the tube.
HABITAT: Middle to upper slopes in the extreme southwestern Cape.

Rice heath derives it name from the slender pale yellow to white flowers that resemble grains of rice coloured with turmeric, a characteristic dish in Cape Malay cuisine.

S4 P4 St8 O   Oct–Jun

Erica coccinea
Tassel heath, Hangertjie

Erect, stiff shrub to 1.2m, with short, needle-like leaves often conspicuously tufted on short branchlets; bearing smooth, yellow, orange or red flowers 6–17mm long hanging in threes at the tip of the branchlets, tubular-conical with a small mouth and lobes, and long brown anthers protrude conspicuously from the tube like little sticks; the minute, scale-like floral bracts are pressed against the base of the calyx at the top of the flower stalks. **HABITAT:** Common on rocky flats and mountains in the southwestern and southern Cape.

Tassel heath is distinguished from the very similar Coathanger heath by having the two minute, scale-like bracts at the top of the wiry flower stalks pressed up against the base of the calyx rather than near the bottom of the stalk. A hand lens is useful for confirming this.

S4 P4 St8 O   Jan–Dec

Erica plukenetii
Coathanger heath, Hangertjie

 Erect shrub to 2m, with long, needle-like leaves, sometimes in tufts; bearing spikes of drooping white, pink, red, green or yellow flowers 12–18mm long, tubular-conical with a small mouth and lobes, and long brown anthers protrude conspicuously from the tube; the minute, scale-like floral bracts are at the base of the flower stalks. **HABITAT:** Widespread in Namaqualand and the southwestern Cape.

The common name derives from the protruding, brown anthers that resemble an old-fashioned, wooden coathanger in miniature. As in all heaths, the pollen is shed from small pores at the tip of the anthers.

Jan–Dec   S4 P4 St8 <u>O</u>

Erica cerinthoides
Fire heath, Rooihaartjie

 Resprouting shrub, mostly compact and to 30cm, but sometimes sparse and to 1.2m, with small, needle-like leaves; bearing densely hairy, orange-red flowers mostly 25–35mm long in a tightly packed cluster at the tip of the branches, swollen-tubular with a constricted mouth and small lobes, and anthers concealed within the tube. **HABITAT:** Sandy flats and slopes, flowering especially after fire, from the southwestern Cape to Mpumalanga.

The flowering stems sprout rapidly from a fire-resistant, woody rootstock and are especially conspicuous on recently burned fynbos slopes. A widespread species, ranging northwards along the Drakensberg escarpment into Mpumalanga. The large, red flowers are pollinated by Malachite Sunbirds.

Jan–Dec   S4 P4 St8 <u>O</u>

Erica mammosa
Ninepin heath, Rooiklossieheide

Erect shrub to 1.5m, with small, needle-like leaves pressed against the surface; bearing clusters of cream, pale green, pink, orange or red flowers 24–25mm long, swollen-tubular flowers with a closed mouth and 4 dimples at the base, and the anthers hidden within the tube. **HABITAT:** Sandy flats and lower mountain slopes in the southwestern Cape.

Ninepin heath occurs in many colours but is always readily recognised by the four dimples at the base of the flower.

S4 P4 St8 <u>O</u>   Nov–May

Erica curviflora
Water heath, Waterbos

Erect, soft to stout shrub to 1.6m with needle-like leaves in whorls of 3; bearing small clusters of hairy or hairless orange, red or yellow flowers 20–30mm long on hairy stalks, tubular with a flaring mouth and lobes, the anthers reaching to the mouth of the tube. **HABITAT:** Widespread in damp or wet areas on flats to high altitude from the southwestern to the Eastern Cape.

S4 P4 St8 <u>O</u>   Jan–Dec

Erica perspicua
Prince-of-Wales heath, Veerheide

Erect shrub to 2m, with small, needle-like leaves in tufts on short side branchlets; bearing long spikes of spreading, hairy, white or pink flowers with white tips, 10–20mm long, tubular and slightly flaring at the mouth with the anthers reaching the top of the tube. **HABITAT:** Marshy slopes and flats between Betty's Bay and Hermanus.

A lovely species that is a favourite among fynbos flower sellers due to its long spikes and local abundance. In early times, the paler, more common forms were known as Sixpenny heath, and the darker, scarcer and thus more expensive forms as Ninepenny heath.

Sep–Apr   S4 P4 St8 <u>O</u>

Erica sessiliflora
Green heath

Erect shrub to 2m, with small, needle-like leaves; bearing short, dense spikes of hairless, almost stalkless, pale green flowers 15–30mm long, tubular with the conspicuously awned anthers reaching the mouth of the tube; the sepals enlarge in fruit and gradually turn red, and the distinctive, fleshy, fruiting inflorescences persist for a long time on the older branches. **HABITAT:** Moist flats and seepages on lower slopes in the southwestern and southern Cape.

A very distinctive species, both on acount of its dense spikes of pistachio-green flowers and its persistent, fleshy fruits.

Jan–Dec   S4 P4 St8 <u>O</u>

Erica abietina
Red heath, Rooiheide

 Erect shrublet to 1.5m, with spreading, needle-like leaves; bearing loose clusters of slightly sticky yellow, orange, red or magenta flowers 10–30mm long, tubular, with the anthers reaching or protruding slightly beyond the mouth of the tube. **HABITAT:** Dry, lower to middle slopes in the southwestern Cape.

A variable species with numerous forms differing in flower size and colour, several on the Cape Peninsula. Most were originally regarded as distinct species.

S4 P4 St8 <u>0</u>   Jan–Dec

Retzia capensis
Retzia, Heuningblom

 Shrublet to 1m, with rod-like, velvety stems resprouting from a woody rootstock; long, narrow leaves in whorls of 4, silky when young and 2-grooved beneath with the margins rolled under; bearing silky, tubular, reddish-orange flowers 45–55mm long, tipped with black, in clusters of up to 3 in the upper leaf axils. **HABITAT:** Sandstone slopes in the extreme southwestern Cape.

The flowers are pollinated by Orange-breasted Sunbirds, and the vernacular name alludes to the abundant nectar that is produced.

S5 P5 St5 <u>0</u>   Sep–Mar

Stilbe ericoides
Heath-leaved stilbe

 Multi-stemmed shrublet to 80cm, with velvety branches resprouting from a woody rootstock, and narrow, ascending leaves in whorls of 4, 2-grooved beneath with the margins rolled under; bearing ±globular spikes of pink or lilac, 2-lipped, funnel-shaped flowers that are hairy in the throat.
HABITAT: Sandy flats or limestone hills along the coast in the southwestern Cape.

The needle-like leaves that characterise many unrelated fynbos shrubs are an example of the process of evolutionary convergence, whereby different organisms come to resemble one another through adaptation to the same environmental conditions. In this case, natural selection has favoured small, hard leaves able to withstand high winds and summer drought.

Apr–Sep   S5 P5 St4 Ō

Stilbe vestita
Silky stilbe

 Multi-stemmed shrublet to 1.2m, with velvety stems resprouting from a woody rootstock, and narrow, ascending or spreading leaves in whorls of 4–6, 2-grooved beneath with the margins rolled under and curved back at the tips; bearing short spikes of white, 2-lipped, funnel-shaped flowers that are hairy in the throat and silky along the margins of the petals.
HABITAT: Sandstone slopes in the extreme southwestern Cape.

The Stilbe family was long thought to be endemic to Cape fynbos, but DNA analysis has revealed that it has close relatives among a few subtropical trees, including *Bowkeria* and *Halleria*. Although the leaves of these trees are broad and flat, they too are arranged in whorls, providing visible evidence of their affinity with *Stilbe*.

Jun–Jan   S5 P5 St4 Ō

S5 P5 St5 <u>O</u>   Jun–Dec

Adenandra uniflora
Chinaflower, Porseleinblom

 Aromatic shrublet to 50cm, with oblong to lance-shaped, gland-dotted leaves 4–14mm long, with the margins rolled under; bearing mostly solitary flowers with waxy, white to pink petals 6–16mm long that are reddish on the reverse, with large, leaf-like sepals; each anther is tipped with a red, knob-like gland and the short-styled ovary is situated in a fleshy cup. **HABITAT:** Sandstone slopes in the extreme southwestern Cape. **SIMILAR:** *Adenandra villosa*, Clustered chinaflower, is a very similar species with flat leaves and heads of 2–6 flowers. The two species are thought to hybridise on the Cape Peninsula.

The common name derives from the glistening, porcelein-like petals.

Adenandra obtusata
Gummy chinaflower

 Aromatic shrublet to 50cm, gummy on the young parts, with thick and leathery, closely overlapping, gland-dotted, oblong leaves 4–6mm long, with the margins rolled under; bearing gummy heads of 1–4 flowers with white petals 8–12mm long that are pink on the reverse; each anther is tipped with a red, knob-like gland and the short-styled ovary is situated in a fleshy cup. **HABITAT:** Limestone hills and flats on the Agulhas Plain.

The dotted glands in the leaves of chinaflowers and the related buchu species indicate their close family affinity to citrus and rue, all of which are characterised by aromatic oils in their foliage.

S5 P5 St5 <u>O</u>   Jan–Dec

Coleonema album
Cape May, Confettibush

 Willowy-stemmed shrub to 2m, with sweet-smelling, gland-dotted, needle-like leaves 12–14mm long; bearing clusters of white flowers 6–7mm in diameter, with the short-styled ovary situated in a fleshy cup. **HABITAT:** Coastal sandstone or granite outcrops in the southwestern Cape. **SIMILAR:** *Coleonema juniperinum*, the Small-flowered Cape May, has smaller flowers 3–4mm in diameter.

An excellent and attractive shrub for coastal gardens. Local fishermen use the aromatic foliage to freshen their hands after working with redbait; it can also be used as an insect repellent.

Aug–Oct   S5 P5 St5 O

Diosma oppositifolia
Bitter buchu, Bitterboegoe

 Many-stemmed shrublet to 1m, from a woody rootstock, with opposite pairs of gland-dotted, needle-like leaves 5–10mm long that are hooked at the tips; bearing small, flat-topped clusters of white, cup-shaped flowers, with the short-styled ovary situated in a conspicuous, greenish, fleshy cup with lobed margins. **HABITAT:** Rocky slopes in the southwestern Cape.

The rather bitter leaves have been used medicinally. The Khoisan traditionally used a wide range of dried and powdered buchu species mixed with animal fat to anoint their bodies as a cleanser and perfume.

Jul–Jan   S5 P5 St5 O

Diosma hirsuta
Red buchu, Rooiboegoe, Kanferboegoe

 Shrublet to 1m, coppicing from a woody rootstock, with alternating, gland-dotted, needle-like leaves 10–22mm long; bearing short racemes of white, cup-shaped flowers that are grouped at the branch tips, with the petals persisting below the fruits, and with the short-styled ovary situated in a conspicuous, greenish, fleshy cup with lobed margins. **HABITAT:** Sandstone and clay slopes in the southwestern and southern Cape.

A floriferous and useful plant for coastal gardens, responding well to pruning, and also used in bouquets.

S5 P5 St5 <u>O</u>   Jul–Nov

Agathosma betulina
Buchu, Boegoe

 Coppicing, broad-leafed shrub to over 2m, with aromatic, oval, gland-dotted leaves, mostly 10–20mm long, minutely toothed on the margins; bearing solitary white to pink flowers in the leaf axils with petals 8–10mm long; the fertile stamens alternate with lance-shaped sterile stamens that resemble the petals, and the style on the ovary is longer than the petals. The fruits are 5-segmented. **HABITAT:** Rocky sandstone slopes on the mountains inland of the West Coast.

Buchu was an important medicinal plant in the Cape pharmacopoeia. The dried leaves were used to treat stomach ailments, or powdered and mixed with sheep fat for anointing the body. It was also once used globally in the flavour and fragrance industries for its blackcurrant-like odour. The vernacular name derives from the original Khoisan.

S5 P5 St5 <u>O</u>   Jun–Nov

Agathosma capensis
Spicy buchu, Anysbuchu

Coppicing shrub to 90cm, with sweetly spice-scented, gland-dotted, needle-like to oval leaves 1.5–7mm long, either hairless or hairy; bearing loose clusters of white, pink or purple flowers with petals 3–5mm long; the fertile stamens alternate with peg-like or lance-shaped sterile stamens resembling small petals, and the style on the ovary is longer than the petals. The fruits are 3-segmented. **HABITAT:** Slopes and flats on shale, granite or coastal sands, less often on acid sand, from Namaqualand to the southern and Eastern Cape.

An attractive species for cultivating in water-wise gardens.

Jan–Dec   S5 P5 St5 O̲

Passerina corymbosa
Common stringbark, Gonna

Willowy shrub or small tree to 2m, with opposite pairs of awl-like leaves 3.5–10mm long in 4 rows, each with a hairy groove beneath; bearing short spikes of small, cream to reddish flowers subtended by tapering oval bracts, the flask-shaped floral tube ±4mm long with a slender neck; there are 8 stamens in 2 unequal whorls protruding well beyond the tube. **HABITAT:** Sandy, often disturbed flats and slopes, such as roadsides, from the southwestern to the Eastern Cape.

Gonna is a Khoisan word applied to various members of the family, the stringy bark of which was used for binding thatch, bundles of firewood, etc. The small flowers with conspicuously protruding anthers are wind-pollinated, releasing clouds of pollen in the morning when brushed.

Oct–Nov   S4 St8 O̅

Cliffortia ruscifolia
Climber's friend, Steekbos

Shrub to 1.5m, with hard, narrowly lance-shaped, stiffly pointed leaves 10–12mm long. The flowers are inconspicuous, with 3 or 4 sepals, and are unisexual with the sexes on the same or different plants: the male flowers with ±12 stamens, and the female flowers with a furrowed, brownish calyx tube 3–4mm long and feathery red stigmas. **HABITAT:** Rocky sandstone soils from Namaqualand to the southern Cape.

The small flowers are adapted to pollination by wind: the male flowers with several anthers dangling out into the air on thread-like filaments, and the female flowers with striking red, feathery stigmas to sweep up pollen grains blown by on the wind. Their English name is somewhat ironic: only someone *in extremis* would grasp these prickly plants.

♂S3 St12 ♀S3 0̄   Aug–Oct

Wahlenbergia subulata
Awl-leaved bluestar, Muistepelkaroo

Erect or sprawling shrublet to 30cm, with hard, spreading, often tufted, narrow or needle-like leaves; bearing shallowly cup-shaped, white to blue flowers ±6mm in diameter with narrow petals that fade to yellow, with sepals that are bulbous below and a mostly hairy ovary. The small, dry fruits open through 5 valve-like flaps at the tip. **HABITAT:** Stony or gravelly lower slopes in the southwestern Cape.

The curious Afrikaans name is a delightful example of the robust and descriptive epithets that were given to plants by early settlers and farming folk who lived close to nature, alluding to the resemblance of the unexpanded stigmas to the nipples of a mouse.

S5 P5 St5 0̄   Oct–Feb

Roella ciliata
Fringed pricklybell

 Erect or sprawling shrublet to 50cm with stiff, awl-like leaves that are whiskered on the margins, often with axillary tufts; bearing solitary, white or blue, cup-shaped flowers 20–30mm in diameter at branch tips, with a dark ring or blotch at base of petal lobes at the mouth of the cup, and a hairless ovary; the floral bracts are larger than the leaves and conspicuously fringed with white whiskers. The small dry fruits open by a lid at the top. **HABITAT:** Stony sandstone slopes in southwestern Cape.

Pollen is shed while flowers are still in bud, collecting outside the closed stigmas, which act as a brush to sweep pollen onto visiting insects. When the flowers open, the anthers are already shrivelled, and a day or two later the stigmas become receptive to pollen brought in from another flower.

Aug–Mar   S5 P5 St5 O̅

Roella incurva
Common pricklybell

 Shrublet to 40cm with stiff, awl-like leaves that are often prickly-toothed on the margins and whiskered, often with axillary tufts; bearing 1 or more white or blue, sometimes pink or red (only Potberg) cup-shaped flowers 20–30mm in diameter at the branch tips, mostly with a dark blotch at the base of the petals at the mouth of the cup, and a hairless ovary; the floral bracts are longer than the leaves, with prickly margins. The small dry fruits open by a lid at the top. **HABITAT:** Sandy lower slopes in the southwestern Cape. **SIMILAR:** *Roella maculata*, Spotted roella, has blotches between the petals and a bristly ovary; *Roella triflora*, Dark-eyed roella, from the Cape Peninsula, has a dark eye in the base of the cup.

Oct–Jan   S5 P5 St5 O̅

Gnidia juniperifolia
Juniper-leaved funnelflower

Erect or spreading shrublet to 50cm, with scattered, narrow to awl-like leaves and slightly broader involucral leaves below the flowers; bearing pairs of yellow, funnel-shaped flowers at the branch tips, with a hairless tube that widens like a funnel towards the mouth, which has 4 membranous petal-scales inserted around it between the 4 flower lobes; there are 8 stamens in 2 whorls of 4 contained within the tube. **HABITAT:** Mountain slopes in the southwestern and southern Cape.

One of several fynbos members of the Daphne family. Funnelflowers all have similar bright yellow flowers with four membranous scales in the mouth.

S4 P4 St8 O̅   Jan–Dec

Gnidia pinifolia
Pine-leaved gnidia

Shrub to 1m with overlapping, alternately inserted, hairless, needle-like to narrowly oblong, sharply pointed leaves, and wider involucral leaves beneath the flower clusters; bearing clusters of ±10 white, salver-shaped flowers at the branch tips that are scented at night, with a slender, silky tube and 4 fleshy, densely silky, white petal-scales inserted around the mouth between the 4 flower lobes; there are 8 stamens in 2 whorls of 4 contained within the tube. **HABITAT:** Sandy flats and lower slopes in the southwestern Cape.

The pure white flowers become fragrant at night, attracting moths as pollinators.

S4 P4 St8 O̅   Jan–Dec

Gnidia oppositifolia
Opposite-leaved gnidia, Basbos

Erect, willowy shrub to 3m with overlapping, opposite pairs of hairless, lance-shaped leaves and similar involucral leaves edged with crimson beneath the flower clusters; bearing clusters of 4–6 pale yellow, salver-shaped flowers at the branch tips, scented at night, with a slender, silky tube, and 4 fleshy, pale yellow petal-scales inserted around the mouth between the 4 petal lobes, turning brown when dry; there are 8 stamens in 2 whorls of 4 contained within the tube. **HABITAT:** Wet sandstone slopes and streambanks from the southwestern to the Eastern Cape.

As in most *Gnidia* species, the bark strips off in tough, stringy strands when the branches are broken, hence the common name (Afrikaans *bas* = bark, *bos* = bush).

Jan–Dec   S4 P4 St8 Ō

Gnidia tomentosa
White gnidia

Shrub to 1m with overlapping, alternately inserted, hairless, oval to lance-shaped leaves that are warty beneath, and similar involucral leaves beneath the flower clusters; bearing clusters of ±6 white, salver-shaped flowers at the branch tips, scented at night, with a slender, silky tube and 4 fleshy, hairy, yellow petal-scales inserted around the mouth between the 4 flower lobes; there are 8 stamens in 2 whorls of 4 contained within the tube. **HABITAT:** Marshy sandstone slopes in the extreme southwestern Cape.

Jan–Dec   S4 P4 St8 Ō

S4 P8 St8 Ō   Jul–Oct

Gnidia squarrosa
Pompombush

Many-branched, willowy shrub to 2m, with alternate, hairless, narrowly lance-shaped leaves, and slightly broader, whorled, involucral leaves that are sometimes hairy on the margins below the flower clusters; bearing head-like clusters of bicoloured, pale creamy, green flowers tinged with pink at the branch tips, with a slender, hairy tube and 8 minute, finger-like petal-scales inserted around the mouth at the base of the 4 flower lobes; there are 8 stamens in 2 whorls of 4 contained within the tube. **HABITAT:** Coastal limestone and sandy slopes from Cape Peninsula to Eastern Cape; common around Hermanus lagoon.

Night-scented flowers make this a lovely plant for fynbos gardens. The flowers are more or less bicoloured.

S4 P8 St4 Ō   Jan–Dec

Struthiola ciliata
Featherhead, Veertjie, Juffertjie-roer-by-die-nag

Erect shrub to 1.5m with wand-like branches and opposite pairs of overlapping, narrowly lance-shaped to oval leaves fringed on the margins; bearing long spikes of cream, pink or reddish, salver-shaped flowers, scented at night, with a sparsely hairy or silky tube 15–20mm long, and 8 silky-tufted petal-scales around the mouth at base of the 4 flower lobes; there is a single whorl of 4 stamens in the tube. **HABITAT:** Sandy flats and lower slopes in Namaqualand and the southwestern Cape.

Veertjie refers either to the plumose flower spikes or the use of the stems as dusters (Afrikaans *vee* = wipe; *veer* = feather). *Juffertjie-roer-by-die nag* (the maiden passes in the night) is a romantic allusion to the scented, pale-flowered shrubs at dusk, evoking the image of a woman in her nightdress.

Hermas villosa
Tinderleaf, Tontelblaar

Robust, single- or few-stemmed shrub to 1m, with leathery, stalkless or shortly stalked, oblong to elliptical, finely toothed leaves that are glossy and hairless above but thickly white-felted beneath; bearing crowded clusters of small cream-coloured, star-like flowers on branched stems, each small sub-cluster usually with a single female or bisexual flower surrounded by several male flowers. The fruits split into 2 flattened and winged halves that are pressed face-to-face. **HABITAT:** Rocky sandstone slopes in the extreme southwestern Cape.

The woolly hairs were scraped from the leaves and, when dried, the floss used for dressing wounds and in tinder boxes, hence the vernacular name.

Dec–May   S5 P5 St5 Ō

Notobubon galbanum
Blisterbush, Bergseldery

Robust, sparsely branched shrub to 3m, with leathery, greyish leaves twice-divided into diamond- to oval-shaped or sometimes 3-lobed, toothed leaflets; bearing small, yellow, star-like flowers in large, rounded, compound clusters on short stems in the leaf axils. The fruits are elliptical, ±6mm long, with the 2 halves face-to-face. **HABITAT:** Rocky sandstone slopes in bush and on forest margins in the southwestern and southern Cape.

The leaves of Blisterbush induce photosensitivity, leading to severe blistering in sunlight. Hikers should avoid brushing against the plant, but if this happens then immediately cover the affected area to exclude sunlight. The leaves have been used medicinally.

Jul–Feb   S5 P5 St5 Ō

S4 St4 <u>0</u>   Jun–Mar

Penaea sarcocolla
Cape fellwort, Vlieëbossie

Sparsely branched shrub with slender stems to 1.5m, coppicing from a woody base, with opposite pairs of leathery, rather waxy, oval to almost diamond-shaped leaves closely overlapping in 4 ranks; bearing short, head-like spikes of large, glossy pink, salver-shaped flowers with 4 petal-like sepals and a cylindrical tube 20–30mm long, subtended by broad, gummy yellowish bracts with finely fringed margins. **HABITAT:** Rocky sandstone slopes in the extreme southwestern Cape.

Fellwort was originally described as a species of *Penaea* but later removed to the separate genus *Saltera*. The relationships among members of this small family are more complex than previously supposed, however, and they are now all placed in the single genus, *Penaea*. The waxy flowers are pollinated by Orange-breasted Sunbirds.

S5 P5 St~ <u>0</u>   Jul–Dec

Anisodontea scabrosa
Sandrose, Sandroos

Shrub to 2m, thinly to densely covered in gland-tipped hairs, with firm-textured, obscurely 3-lobed or elliptical, toothed leaves, and 1 or more pink, hibiscus-like flowers in the upper leaf axils, with the numerous stamens joined together into a hairy column surrounding the style; the calyx cup is surrounded at the base by a whorl of 3–5 narrow, leaf-like bracts. The dry, drum-shaped fruits split into numerous narrow, wedge-shaped segments. **HABITAT:** Coastal sands and granite outcrops from the West Coast to KwaZulu-Natal.

A tough plant, ideal for coastal gardens.

Hibiscus aethiopicus
Dwarf hibiscus, Wildestokroos

 Dwarf subshrub with sprawling stems to 30cm from a woody rootstock, with firm-textured, oval to elliptical leaves, 3- to 5-veined from the base and sometimes coarsely toothed at ends, hairy beneath but almost hairless above; bearing solitary cream to yellow, typical hibiscus-like flowers on slender stalks in the leaf axils, often with a dark eye, with numerous stamens joined together into a column surrounding the style, each flower lasting a single day and fading orange; the calyx cup is surrounded at the base by a whorl of 10–12 narrow, leaf-like bracts. The dry, globose fruits split open. **HABITAT:** Stony sandstone or clay slopes from the southwestern Cape to KwaZulu-Natal.

Preliminary tests suggest that Dwarf hibiscus may contain chemicals that provide protection against the effects of haemorrhagic snake venoms.

Jun–Feb   S5 P5 St~ <u>O</u>

Hermannia pinnata
Creeping dollsrose, Kruip poprosie

 Shrublet with rough, creeping stems to 15cm, often forming mats, with narrow, almost hairless leaves that are sometimes deeply lobed above and often spuriously whorled because the stipules at the base of each leaf are divided into 2 or 3 narrow, leaf-like lobes; bearing nodding, sweetly scented, bell-shaped, yellow to pale orange flowers with furled petals on slender stalks in the leaf axils. **HABITAT:** Sandy coastal flats and dunes along the West Coast.

A quick-growing, tough plant, ideal for coastal gardens, rockeries and hanging baskets, producing masses of fragrant flowers.

Aug–Oct   S5 P5 St5 <u>O</u>

S5 P5 St5 <u>0</u>   Sep–Oct

Hermannia trifoliata
Agulhas dollsrose, Tandebossie

Grey-green shrublet with stiffly erect branches to 40cm, and ascending, closely overlapping, stalkless, wedge-shaped leaves subtended at the base by large, leafy stipules so that the leaves appear to be in tufts of 3; bearing terminal clusters of nodding, urn-shaped, orange to red flowers with closely furled petals ±10mm long, flaring sharply at the tips with a pin-hole throat and a ±inflated, papery calyx. **HABITAT:** Coastal limestone soils in the southern Cape.

S5 P5 St5 <u>0</u>   Mar–Dec

Gomphocarpus cancellatus
Broad-leaved cottonbush, Katoenbos, Gansiebos

Robust shrub to 1.5m with hairy stems, exuding milky white latex when damaged, and opposite pairs of leathery, oblong to elliptical leaves that are rounded at the base; bearing nodding clusters of cream-coloured flowers with a fleshy, 5-lobed column in the centre. The fruits are swollen and egg-shaped with tapering tips and covered in fleshy projections. **HABITAT:** Stony slopes from southern Namibia to the Eastern Cape.

The silky tufts of hairs on the seeds, which give the species its common names, are effective aids in their dispersal. The milky latex contains alkaloids and the roots have been used medicinally.

Gomphocarpus fruticosus
Wetland cottonbush, Vleiklapper

Willowy shrub 1–3m tall, branching mainly from the base, exuding milky latex when damaged, with opposite pairs of narrow leaves that taper gradually towards the base; bearing nodding clusters of cream-coloured flowers with a fleshy, 5-lobed column in the centre. The fruits are swollen and egg-shaped with tapering tips and covered in fleshy projections.
HABITAT: Disturbed areas throughout southern Africa and elsewhere.

A popular garden plant that is highly attractive to butterflies – the flowers for their nectar and the foliage as the food plant for the larvae of the African monarch. The balloon-like fruits are striking in floral arrangements. The dried, ground leaves are used as snuff and an emetic.

Nov–Apr   S5 P5 St5 <u>O</u>

Limonium peregrinum
Sea-lavender, Strandroos, Papierblom

Shrub to 1m with bright green, paddle-shaped leaves 40–80mm long concentrated at the branch tips, with a rough and sometimes pitted surface; bearing flat-topped clusters of pink-and-magenta flowers, with a papery, salver-shaped calyx with 10 scalloped lobes, 15–17mm in diameter, and 5 wedge-shaped petals that are slightly creased or wrinkled; each flower has 5 thread-like styles.
HABITAT: Coastal dunes in Namaqualand and on the West Coast.

The dry, papery calyces persist for a long time, making the species useful for fresh and dried flower arrangements. A tough plant that is valuable in windy coastal gardens. The leaves contain numerous glands which excrete excess salt, allowing the plants to survive in salty soils that would kill most other species.

Aug–Jan   S5 P5 St5 <u>O</u>

Chironia baccifera
Christmas berry, Aambeibossie

Tangled shrublet to 1m, with narrow, spreading leaves arranged alternately; bearing small, pink, star-shaped flowers with a short tube 3–5mm long that is constricted above the ovary. The fruits are bright red, fleshy berries. **HABITAT:** Sandy flats and slopes from Namaqualand to KwaZulu-Natal.

Christmas berry was used medicinally but is potentially toxic. The name *Aambeibossie* derives from its use in the treatment of haemorrhoids (Afrikaans *aambeie*), primarily on account of a fancied resemblance of its fleshy fruits to this painful condition, following the medieval 'doctrine of signatures'. It was also used as a purgative and general tonic. It is a fine ornamental plant, both in flower and in fruit.

S5 P5 St5 <u>O</u>   Nov–Feb

Orphium frutescens
Searose

Velvety shrublet to 80cm, with opposite pairs of leathery, narrow or paddle-shaped leaves that have the margins rolled under; bearing 1 or 2 glossy pink flowers in the upper leaf axils, with bright yellow, twisted anthers that open through pores at the tips, and a style that is deflexed downwards. **HABITAT:** Coastal sands and pans in the southwestern and southern Cape.

Searose is a fine garden plant, able to grow close to the sea and coping easily with wind, sand and brackish soils. The attractive flowers are long-lasting. The distinctive, twisted anthers release their pollen from pores at their tips, like a salt-cellar, when vibrated or buzzed by carpenter bees, which grasp the anthers and rapidly vibrate their wings, causing the pollen to be ejected onto the insect.

S5 P5 St5 <u>O</u>   Nov–Feb

Pelargonium fulgidum
Scarlet storksbill, Rooimalva

 Succulent-stemmed shrublet to 40cm with unevenly once-divided, densely silvery-silky leaves 10–17cm in diameter, and short flowering stems bearing a cluster of 4–9 2-lipped flowers 15–20mm in diameter on stalks 20–40mm long, with bright red, unmarked petals. The fruits are awl-like. **HABITAT:** Rocky slopes, often coastal granite, in Namaqualand and the West Coast.

The bright red flowers are pollinated by sunbirds, which probe the narrow, floral tubes that form part of the floral stalks for the traces of nectar that they contain.

Jun–Nov   S5 P5 St10 O

Pelargonium betulinum
Beech-leaved storksbill, Kanferblaar

 Shrub to 1.5m, with oval to elliptic, somewhat leathery leaves ±20mm long, and clusters of up to 6 flowers ±50mm in diameter, on short stalks 3–8mm long in the leaf axils, with white to pink petals, the larger upper 2 with red markings. The fruits are awl-like. **HABITAT:** Coastal dunes in the southwestern and southern Cape.

The vernacular name derives from the camphor-like odour of the crushed leaves. The vapour from steaming the leaves was inhaled as a treatment for coughs and other chest complaints.

Aug–Jan   S5 P5 St10 O

Pelargonium cucullatum
Mallow-flowered storksbill, Wildemalva

Shrub to 2m, with roughly hairy, more or less round, toothed leaves ±7cm in diameter, and clusters of up to 13 showy flowers ±40mm in diameter, on short stalks 5–12mm long, with widely overlapping, pinkish-purple petals, the upper 2 with purple markings. The fruits are awl-like.
HABITAT: Sandstone and granite slopes along the coast in the southwestern Cape.

This is one of the parent species of the cultivated regal pelargoniums. It was an important medicinal plant and was also grown as an ornamental hedgerow in 19th-century Cape Town. Alas, no longer.

S5 P5 St10 O   Sep–Feb

Pelargonium capitatum
Seaside storksbill, Rose-scented pelargonium, Kusmalva

Sprawling shrublet to 50cm, with softly velvety, aromatic, rounded, lobed and crisped leaves ±5cm in diameter, and velvety stalks bearing dense, head-like clusters of up to 20 2-lipped flowers 15–25mm in diameter on short stalks 3–8mm long, with pink petals, the slightly larger upper 2 streaked with red. The fruits are awl-like.
HABITAT: Coastal dunes and flats from the West Coast to KwaZulu-Natal.

The Rose-scented pelargonium is cultivated for its essential oils, known confusingly as oil of geranium. The fresh leaves can be rubbed directly onto the skin as an emollient, and a tea made from them was also used medicinally.

S5 P5 St10 O   Sep–Oct

Pelargonium myrrhifolium
Myrrh-leaved storksbill

Sprawling shrublet to 50cm, with oval leaves ±5 × 3cm and twice-divided into thread-like or linear to ribbon-shaped segments, and short stems bearing clusters of up to 5 2-lipped flowers, 20–25mm in diameter, on short stalks 4–10mm long, with white to pink petals, the upper two much wider and feathered with red. The fruits are awl-like.
HABITAT: Open places on stony sand from Namaqualand to the Eastern Cape.

As in all members of the Geranium family, the awl-like fruits split from the base at maturity into five segments, each rolling up like a watch-spring to release the seed contained within. Each seed is equipped with a single plumed bristle that alternately coils and uncoils with drying and wetting, acting as a bore to drill the seed into the soil.

Aug–Feb   S5 P5 St10 <u>O</u>

Melianthus major
Honeyflower, Kruidjie-roer-my-nie

Foetid shrub to 2m, with large leaves with a distinct greyish bloom, divided into unequally-sided, toothed leaflets, with large, leafy stipules at base of the leaf stalks; the large, long-stalked racemes bear whorls of 2–4, very asymmetrical flowers, each flower with 5 large, pointed sepals and 5 small, reddish petals shorter than the maroon to greenish sepals. The bladder-like, 4-winged fruits are hairless.
HABITAT: Mostly along streams in the southwestern and Eastern Cape.

A valued foliage plant in cool, temperate gardens. The leaves release a foetid smell when touched, signalling their toxicity. The Afrikaans name means 'do-not-disturb-herb'. The fresh leaves and roots were used medicinally as an antiseptic. Birds visit the flowers for the copious nectar.

Aug–Sep   S5 P5 St4 <u>O</u>

Lobostemon glaucophyllus
Smooth-leaved pyjamabush

Shrublet, 0.5–1m, with hairless, reddish young branches and bluish-green, narrowly lance-shaped leaves that are hairy only along the midrib and margins; bearing open clusters of widely funnel-shaped, blue to pink flowers 7–15mm long, without any hairs on the outside of the petals and with all of the sepals similar in shape. **HABITAT:** Sandy flats and slopes in the southwestern Cape.

One of only a few species of pyjamabush with flowers that are completely hairless on the outside. The vernacular name references the striped pink-and-blue flowers of some species, which suggested the flannelette that was traditionally used for pyjamas.

S5 P5 St5 <u>O</u>   Jul–Oct

Lobostemon fruticosus
Common pyjamabush, Agtdaegeneesbos

Shrublet, 0.5–1m, with short-haired branches and rough-haired, elliptical or oval leaves; bearing clusters of funnel-shaped, blue-and-pink or pink-and-red flowers 15–25mm long that are hairy outside along the midribs. **HABITAT:** Stony flats in Namaqualand and the southwestern Cape.

This very attractive plant was widely respected as a traditional herbal remedy: a tea made from the leaves was used as a vermifuge, and the fresh leaves were used in combination with other herbs as an antiseptic ointment. The Afrikaans name alludes to the belief that it could heal all sorts of ailments within eight days.

S5 P5 St5 <u>O</u>   May–Dec

Lobostemon montanus
Mountain pyjamabush

Shrub, 1–2m, with silver-haired, oval to lance-shaped leaves; bearing clusters of funnel-shaped, blue or turquoise flowers 15–25mm long that are hairy outside along the midribs. **HABITAT:** Coastal sandstone slopes in the extreme southwestern Cape.

This attractive plant, easily seen on the mountains of the Cape Peninsula, is quick growing and a welcome addition to coastal gardens due to its tolerance of salt-laden winds.

Jul–Sep	S5 P5 St5 <u>O</u>

Lobelia coronopifolia
Large-flowered lobelia

Tufted shrublet to 30cm, with somewhat sprawling, short-haired stems branching from the base, and narrow to lance-shaped, deeply toothed or lobed leaves 5–10mm wide, with the margins slightly rolled under; bearing 1 to a few large, hairless, dark blue, pink or white, 2-lipped, salver-shaped flowers 15–30mm long, on wiry, leafless stalks 10–28cm long, with the anthers joined to one another. **HABITAT:** Sandy and stony flats and lower slopes in the southwestern Cape. **SIMILAR:** *Lobelia tomentosa* is very similar, but has finely velvety flowers.

The anthers in lobelias are joined along their sides and shed their pollen into the tube thus formed. The elongating style acts like a piston to force the pollen out of the anther tube and onto a visiting pollinator.

Oct–Apr	S5 P5 St5 <u>O</u>

Lobelia valida
Limestone lobelia, Galjoenblom

 Soft, leafy shrublet with rod-like stems to 60cm, and overlapping, broadly paddle-shaped, toothed, leathery leaves 10–15mm wide; bearing dense racemes of showy, hairless, blue, 2-lipped, salver-shaped flowers 10–15mm long, with the anthers joined to one another. **HABITAT:** Coastal limestone hills on the Agulhas Plain.

A fine ornamental species for coastal gardens. Plants should be replaced every few years for a continuing show, either from seed or from cuttings.

S5 P5 St5 O̅   **Nov–Apr**

Salvia lutea
Brown sage, Bruinsalie, Strandsalie

 Aromatic, greyish-green shrub to 2m, with square stems and opposite pairs of paddle-shaped, sometimes toothed leaves; bearing pairs of golden-brown, 2-lipped flowers 30–50mm long, with a boat-shaped upper lip ±25mm long; the 5-lobed calyx is short-haired and gland-dotted, and enlarges conspicuously in fruit. 4 small, round nutlets are contained within the enlarged, papery calyx. **HABITAT:** Coastal scrub from Namaqualand to Eastern Cape.

Brown sage was formerly known as *Salvia africana-lutea*. Each flower has only two stamens that arch up under the upper hood. The stamens are hinged near the base, with a pedal-like extension. When this is depressed by a bird probing the flowers, it acts as a lever causing the upper arm of the stamen to swing down and brush pollen onto the bird.

S5 P5 St2 O̲   **Jun–Dec**

Salvia lanceolata
Rusty sage, Rooisalie

Aromatic, greyish shrub to 2m, with square stems and opposite pairs of lance- or paddle-shaped, sometimes toothed leaves; bearing pairs of dull rose to grey-blue 2-lipped flowers 25–35mm long, with a boat-shaped upper lip ±17mm long; the 5-lobed calyx is short-haired and gland-dotted, and enlarges conspicuously in fruit. 4 small, round nutlets are contained within the enlarged, papery calyx. **HABITAT:** Mainly coastal areas, in fynbos, on deep, acidic sands and rock outcrops, in Namaqualand and the southwestern Cape.

Rusty sage is an excellent garden plant, and attractive to nectar-feeding birds that visit the flowers. It is known to hybridise with Silky blue sage where they co-occur, resulting in a range of intermediate flower forms (shown at right).

Sep–Jun   S5 P5 St2 <u>O</u>

Salvia africana
Silky blue sage, Bloublomsalie

Grey shrub to 2m, with square stems and opposite pairs of softly hairy, paddle-shaped, sometimes toothed leaves; bearing whorls of mauve to blue or pink 2-lipped flowers with darker spots, 16–28mm long, with a boat-shaped upper lip; the 5-lobed calyx is glandular-silky and enlarges in fruit. 4 small, round nutlets are contained within the enlarged, papery calyx. **HABITAT:** Sandy flats and slopes in Namaqualand and the southwestern Cape.

Silky blue sage was formerly known as *Salvia africana-caerulea*. The leaves were used medicinally and to flavour food. The species is an excellent garden plant.

Jun–Jan   S5 P5 St2 <u>O</u>

S10–20 P5 St4 <u>O</u>   May–Nov

Ballota africana
Horehound, Kattekruie

Aromatic, soft-textured, greyish shrublet to 1.2m, with square stems and opposite pairs of softly hairy, heart-shaped leaves with a quilted surface and regularly toothed margins; bearing pink to purple 2-lipped flowers 10–15mm long in dense, globose clusters in the leaf axils; the funnel-shaped calyx is hairy on the inside as well as on the outside, with 10–20 spreading and often sharply pointed or awned teeth. **HABITAT:** Rocky or disturbed places in southern Africa.

Infusions or tinctures of the leaves of *Ballota africana* were used medicinally as a sedative. The Afrikaans vernacular name *Kattekruie*, or 'cat-herb', references the European catnip, *Nepeta cataria*.

S8–10 P5 St4 <u>O</u>   Nov–Jul

Leonotis leonurus
Minaretflower, Wildedagga

Roughly hairy shrub to 2m, with stiffly erect, square stems and opposite pairs of narrowly lance-shaped, toothed leaves; bearing ball-like whorls of velvety orange 2-lipped flowers 40–50mm long, with a long upper lip and small lower lobes that are curled back; the cup-shaped calyx is sharply 8–10-toothed. **HABITAT:** Forest margins, rough grassland and roadsides from the southwestern Cape to Gauteng. **SIMILAR:** Basil-leaved minaret flower, *Leonotis ocymifolia*, has oval, toothed leaves with a long, slender stalk and a 2-lipped calyx.

An excellent garden plant, attracting sunbirds to the flowers. The dried leaves were used medicinally but are not known to be narcotic, or even tolerable, as a tobacco substitute, despite the Afrikaans vernacular name.

Anemone tenuifolia
Cape anemone, Syblom

Perennial to 40cm with a basal tuft of leathery leaves that are twice- or thrice-divided into triangular, 3-toothed segments with the margins rolled under; with woolly flower stalks bearing solitary, large, white to pink flowers with deciduous petal-like sepals, 20–40mm long, the outer ones silky beneath. The small, dry fruits are densely hairy. **HABITAT:** Moist sandstone slopes in the southwestern and southern Cape.

This species was known for many years as *Anemone capensis*, but that name is botanically incorrect. Although called petals for convenience, the colourful segments of the flowers are technically sepals, and true petals are lacking. Although anemones are mostly native to the northern hemisphere, DNA findings suggest that the ancestor of the southern African members arrived here from South America.

Jun–Feb   S~ St~ 0

Anemone vesicatoria
Blisterleaf, Katjiedrieblaar, Tandpynblaar

Perennial to 1.2m with a basal tuft of hairless, leathery leaves, once- or twice-divided into finely toothed, oval segments; with flowering stalks not much longer than the leaves, bearing clusters of white to yellowish-green flowers with deciduous petal-like sepals, 10–20mm long. Fruits are small, fleshy berries. **HABITAT:** Scrub or wooded ravines from the southwestern to the Eastern Cape.

The fresh leaves and roots are an irritant, causing blistering, and were used medicinally. This is one of a group of several small-flowered species that were previously treated as the genus *Knowltonia* on account of their slightly fleshy fruits, but are now understood to belong to the same lineage as the Cape anemone. The fleshy fruits are consumed and dispersed by birds.

Aug–Oct   S~ St~ 0

Drosera capensis
Cape sundew, Doublom

Rhizomatous perennial to 30cm with a distinct, woody stem below the leaves, which are strap-shaped to elliptical and covered in sticky glands and tentacles; the slender flowering stalk curves outwards from the plant at the base, bearing a drooping, 1-sided raceme of several pink to magenta flowers 20–30mm in diameter. **HABITAT:** Marshy sandstone in the southwestern and southern Cape.

The flowers open for only a few hours each day. The sticky, dew-like tentacles on the leaves entrap small insects and digest them as a source of nitrogen, which is in short supply in the acid sandstone soils in which the plants thrive.

S5 P5 St5 <u>O</u>   Dec–Jan

Drosera cistiflora
Rose-flowered sundew, Snotrosie

Slender perennial to 40cm with or without basal leaves but always with slender leaves scattered up the stem, all covered in sticky glands and tentacles; bearing a few large, white, creamy yellow, pink, mauve, purple or red flowers 30–40mm in diameter with a dark centre. **HABITAT:** Damp, sandy flats and seeps from Namaqualand to the southern Cape.

Although the species is variable in flower colour, individual populations are constant. Pink or mauve are most common but the striking red form is very rare.

S5 P5 St5 <u>O</u>   Aug–Sep

Dianthus albens
Wild pink, Wilde-angelier

Loosely tufted or sprawling perennial to 40cm, with narrow, grass-like leaves in opposite pairs joined at the base into a short sheath, and slender flowering stalks bearing several white to purple flowers, with small scale-like bracts at the base of the tubular calyx, 12–18mm long; the calyx encloses the stalk-like bases of the narrowly paddle-shaped petals, which are smooth or toothed along the outer edges, and the stamens are also partially enclosed within the calyx tube. **HABITAT:** Sandy flats and slopes, often coastal, from the southwestern to the Eastern Cape.

Dianthus caryophyllaceus from the Mediterranean is the florists' carnation. It was first cultivated at the Cape by Jan van Riebeeck, who established a refreshment station there in 1652 at the behest of the Dutch East India Company. This paved the way for European settlement of the region.

Sep–Feb | S5 P5 St10 <u>O</u>

Silene undulata
Cape campion, Wildetabak

Soft perennial to 1m, covered in short, gland-tipped hairs mixed with longer straggling hairs at the base of the stem, with opposite pairs of lance-shaped leaves; a widely branched flowering stem bears a few white to pale pink flowers with a tubular calyx, 18–45mm long, that encloses the stalk-like bases of the notched petals; the fragrant flowers open at night. The club-shaped fruits are partially enclosed in the calyx tube and open by means of small, tooth-like flaps at the tip. **HABITAT:** Slopes and flats throughout southern and tropical Africa.

Moths visit the open flowers at night. Several closely allied species of campion occur along the West Coast. Recent study suggests that they evolved from a single, ancient, long-distance introduction from the northern hemisphere, where the remaining nearly related species occur.

Aug–Sep | S5 P5 St10 <u>O</u>

Heliophila africana
Hairy sunflax

More or less rough-haired, annual herb to 40cm, often somewhat sprawling, with lance-shaped leaves that are often lobed or toothed above, and racemes of blue or mauve 4-petalled flowers with hairless or hairy sepals. The narrow fruits are not beaded and are 13–100mm long. **HABITAT:** Sandy flats in Namaqualand and the southwestern Cape.

Sunflax is allied to cabbage and other cruciferous plants, so named for the cross-shaped flowers with four petals arranged like the arms of a crucifix.

S4 P4 St6 <u>O</u>   Aug–Nov

Heliophila coronopifolia
Common sunflax

Annual herb with stiffly erect stems to 60cm, and thread-like or variously lobed leaves, and branched racemes of blue 4-petalled flowers with a white or greenish centre and hairless, purplish sepals. The slender, beaded fruits are 30–90mm long. **HABITAT:** Widespread on sandy flats and slopes, often forming massed displays in Namaqualand and the southwestern Cape.

The flowers open on warm or sunny days but remain tighly closed at night or during inclement weather.

S4 P4 St6 <u>O</u>   Aug–Oct

Linum africanum
African flax

Perennial with slender stems to 50cm, from a persistent woody base, with opposite pairs of narrowly lance-shaped leaves and loosely branched, flowering stems of yellow flowers flushed red on the reverse, the rapidly deciduous petals furled like an umbrella in bud; the ovary is topped with 5 thread-like styles that are joined below for up to half their length. **HABITAT:** Sandstone and limestone slopes and flats in the southwestern and southern Cape.

A tough plant, ideal for coastal gardens. Blue-flowered *Linum usitatissimum* from Europe is the common flax or linseed.

Sep–Jan   S5 P5 St5 <u>O</u>

Sebaea exacoides
Painted yellowwort, Naeltjiesblom

Annual herb to 30cm with opposite pairs of oval leaves, the stem branching above into a flat-topped cluster of salver-shaped yellow or cream flowers with orange streaks in the throat; the narrow floral tube is 6–19mm long and almost as long as the petals, which are tightly furled in bud; the sepals are strongly winged on the back. **HABITAT:** Moist, sandy flats and slopes in the southwestern Cape.

A distant relative of gentian. The Afrikaans name is possibly derived from a superficial resemblance of the flower buds to cloves. It is certainly not for their fragrance, for they have none.

Aug–Oct   S5 P5 St5 <u>O</u>

Oxalis pes-caprae
Cape sorrel, Geelsuring

Bulbous perennial, stemless with leaves in a basal tuft, each divided into 3 wedge-shaped, notched leaflets, usually hairless above and hairy beneath; bearing a cluster of 3–20 canary yellow, funnel-shaped flowers with separate petals that are tightly furled in bud and at night. **HABITAT:** Widespread and common from Namaqualand to the Eastern Cape.

Plants are rich in oxalic acid, giving them a sour taste. The leaves were used in stews, particularly traditional *waterblommetjiebredie* (mutton stew) and as a vermifuge. The petals were used as a source of yellow dye. Cape sorrel is widely naturalised in the Mediterranean region and elsewhere, under a variety of names, including Bermuda grass and Sourgrass.

S5 P5 St10 <u>O</u>   June–Oct

Oxalis obtusa
Veined sorrel, Geeloogsuring

Cormous perennial, stemless with a basal tuft of leaves, each divided into 3 broadly wedge- or heart-shaped leaflets that are hairless or hairy; bearing solitary pink, brick-red, orange or yellow, funnel-shaped flowers with darker veins and a yellow tube on a jointed stalk that is covered with down-facing hairs, with separate petals that are tightly furled in bud and at night. **HABITAT:** Mostly damp clay and granite slopes from Namaqualand to the Eastern Cape; widespread and common.

Veined sorrel varies in flower colour but is easily recognised by the jointed flower stalk covered in down-facing hairs, and the darkly veined flowers with widely spreading petals.

S5 P5 St10 <u>O</u>   Jun–Oct

Oxalis purpurea
Grand duchess sorrel, Grootsuring

 Stemless perennial with leaves divided into 3 heart-shaped leaflets with fine hairs on the margins, purple beneath, developing black streaks when dry; bearing solitary, large purple, pink, yellow or white flowers with a yellow tube.
HABITAT: Widespread and common on damp flats and slopes from Namaqualand to the Eastern Cape.

An attractive species worth cultivating for its large flowers, which make splashes of colour on lawns in and around Cape Town in the spring. Each flower has 10 stamens in two series of five, at different heights, with stigmas at a third level. Any individual flower thus has one of three possible conformations of the stamens and styles. This structural differentiation is thought to encourage cross-pollination.

May–Sep   S5 P5 St10 O

Oxalis hirta
Hairy sorrel

 Cormous perennial with a leafy, often branching stem 5–30cm tall, with stalkless, often tufted, grey-green leaves divided into 3 narrowly elliptical, folded leaflets that are hairy beneath; bearing solitary mauve, magenta or white funnel-shaped flowers with a yellow, sometimes long and cylindrical tube, and petals that are tightly furled in bud and at night. **HABITAT:** Flats and lower slopes along the West Coast.

This is a species worth cultivating, with attractive leafy stems rather like miniature bottlebrushes. Long-tubed forms are most common in the Olifants River Valley between Citrusdal and Klawer.

Apr–Jun   S5 P5 St10 O

Wahlenbergia capensis
Cape bluebell

Erect, annual herb to 50cm, covered in coarse hairs, with paddle-shaped to elliptical, wavy or toothed leaves mostly scattered up the stem; bearing solitary, bowl-shaped, pale blue flowers on long stems, with a dark, hairy centre often surrounded by a paler halo; the ovary is bristly and the stigma has 5 broad, petal-like lobes. Small, dry fruits open through 5 valve-like flaps at the tip. **HABITAT:** Sandstone slopes and flats in southwestern and southern Cape.

The dark eye in the centre of the flower mimics one of the monkey beetle species that are common in the region, attracting other individuals to the flower. As the beetles crawl about on the flowers, they collect and deposit pollen from their furry bodies. Several fynbos species exploit this behaviour by developing dark 'beetle markings' on their flowers.

S5 P5 St5 Ō | Sep–Dec

Geranium incanum
Carpet geranium, Amarabossie, Vrouetee

Diffuse, trailing perennial with long-stalked leaves, the blades divided to the base into 3–7 deeply lobed segments that are hairless or sparsely hairy above, with dense white hairs beneath; bearing 1 or 2 pink to mauve (rarely white with pink veins) radially symmetrical flowers 15–30mm in diameter on slender stalks in the leaf axils, with 5 rapidly deciduous petals. The fruits are awl-like. **HABITAT:** Sandy and stony soils along coast from Cape Peninsula to Eastern Cape.

The leaves were used as a medicinal tea, and several of the vernacular names allude to this, including *Amarabossie* (Latin *amara* = bitter, Afrikaans *bossie* = shrub), and *Vrouetee* (Afrikaans *vroue* = women, *tee* = tea). Some forms are popular garden plants.

S5 P5 St10 Ō | Jul–Dec

Monsonia speciosa
Lady Monson's parasol, Sambreeltjie

Sprawling perennial producing annual stems from a short rhizome, with long-stalked, toothed to finely divided, almost hairless leaves, and slender stalks bearing solitary, large, white to pink or bicoloured, radially symmetrical flowers, 25–65mm in diameter, with 5 creased or veined petals unevenly toothed along the edges and closing tightly at night. **HABITAT:** Clay and granite slopes and flats in the southwestern Cape.

Named for Lady Anne Monson, who collected wild flowers around Cape Town in 1774. Swedish botanist, Carl Linnaeus, wrote her a letter asking (metaphorically, no doubt, as both were married) to join her in the 'procreation of just one little daughter to bear witness to our love – a little *Monsonia*, through which your fame would live forever in the Kingdom of Flora'.

Aug–Nov   S5 P5 St15 <u>O</u>

Pelargonium triste
Clove-scented storksbill, Kaneeltjie

Tuberous perennial to 50cm, with a basal cluster of large, soft-haired leaves up to 30cm long, finely twice- or thrice-divided into narrow segments, and long, silky stems bearing a cluster of up to 20 weakly 2-lipped flowers, 15–18mm in diameter, on stalks 25–35mm long, with pale yellow petals variously marked with maroon to black. The fruits are awl-like. **HABITAT:** Sandy flats and lower slopes, often coastal, from Namaqualand to the southern Cape.

The dull-coloured flowers are unscented during the day but become strongly clove-scented at night to attract pollinating moths. The powdered tuberous root was used as a purgative.

Aug–Feb   S5 P5 St10 <u>O</u>

S2 P4 St4 <u>O</u>   Aug–Nov

Dischisma ciliatum
Fringed false slugwort

Sprawling perennial herb to 40cm, with spreading, narrow to elliptical, toothed leaves; bearing elongated spikes of white, 1-lipped flowers with a funnel-shaped tube that is split down the front and fanned above into a 4-lobed lip, subtended by fringed bracts; the 2-lobed calyx is joined to the subtending bract. The fruit splits horizontally into two segments. **HABITAT:** Rocky slopes and flats in the southwestern and southern Cape.

S5 P5 St4 <u>O</u>   Sep–Mar

Pseudoselago serrata
Broad-leaved powderpuff

Stout, leafy perennial to 40cm, with opposite pairs of closely overlapping, oval leaves, sparsely toothed on the margins, with the tips curved over, and that continue down the stem in narrow wings; bearing dense, flat-topped clusters of mauve, funnel-shaped, 2-lipped flowers. **HABITAT:** Mountain slopes in the extreme southwestern Cape. **SIMILAR:** *Pseudoselago pulchra*, from the coastal mountains around Hermanus, has closely toothed leaves that are not curved at the tips.

Zaluzianskya villosa
Southern mauve drumsticks,
Verfblommetjie

 Annual herb to 30cm, with densely hairy, rather blunt, lance-shaped leaves; bearing crowded spikes of white to mauve, salver-shaped flowers with a yellow or red star in the centre, with a slender tube 10–25mm long and deeply notched petals; the calyx is tubular and strongly ribbed and pleated. **HABITAT:** Sandy flats along the coast in the southwestern Cape. **SIMILAR:** *Zaluzianskya affinis*, from north of Saldanha, has sharper, almost hairless leaves.

The fresh flowers have a yellow star in the centre to guide pollinators to the nectar. The star turns reddish after pollination, making it invisible to insects, which mostly cannot see red. This prevents wasted repeat visits.

Jul–Nov   S5 P5 St2 0

Zaluzianskya capensis
Cape drumsticks, Nightphlox

 Annual or short-lived perennial to 30cm, with toothed, lance-shaped leaves; bearing spikes of white, salver-shaped flowers that are dull maroon on the outside, opening only at night, with a slender tube 25–40mm long and deeply notched petals; the calyx is tubular, strongly ribbed and pleated. **HABITAT:** Sandy and stony places, from Namaqualand to the Eastern Cape.

The flowers are adapted to pollination by moths, remaining closed and almost invisible during the day but expanding at dusk to reveal the white upper surface of the petals and emitting a sweet fragrance. Closed flowers resemble tiny drumsticks, with petals forming a knob-like head at the end of the slender floral tube.

Jul–Oct   S5 P5 St4 0

S5 P5 St4 <u>O</u>   Jul–Sep

Nemesia bicornis
Delta-fruit nemesia

Annual herb to 80cm, with narrowly lance-shaped, toothed to lobed leaves; bearing widely branched racemes of small, white to pale lilac, snapdragon-like flowers with grey veins, with 4 velvety swellings at the base of the lower lip and a 4mm-long spur, slightly swollen at the tip. The fruits are triangular. **HABITAT:** Coastal sands in Namaqualand and the southwestern Cape.

Characterised by its branched stems of white or pale lilac flowers and small, triangular fruits.

S5 P5 St4 <u>O</u>   Aug–Nov

Nemesia affinis
Varicoloured nemesia

Annual herb to 30cm, with elliptical to lance-shaped, toothed leaves; bearing shortly branched racemes of unicoloured or bicoloured, white, blue, yellow or sometimes red, snapdragon-like flowers, with a raised cream to yellow palate at the base of the lower lip bearing 2 velvety swellings, and a spur 3–5mm long. The fruits are as long as, or slightly longer than, they are wide. **HABITAT:** Sandy and granite slopes and flats from southern Namibia to the Eastern Cape.

A popular garden annual. A striking, bicoloured, white-and-blue form is marketed under the name *Nemesia versicolor* 'KLM', alluding to the livery of the Royal Dutch airline.

Nemesia cheiranthus
Horned nemesia

Annual herb to 40cm, with lance-shaped, lightly toothed leaves; bearing shortly branched racemes of bicoloured, snapdragon-like flowers with white, horn-like upper petals, sometimes marked with purple, and a bright yellow lower lip that has a slightly raised palate at the base bearing 2 velvety swellings, with a spur 3–5mm long. The fruits are as long as they are wide. **HABITAT**: Sandy slopes and flats in Namaqualand and the interior West Coast.

A very pretty species, easily recognised by its long, narrow, horn-like upper petals.

Aug–Sep   S5 P5 St4 <u>O</u>

Nemesia barbata
Bearded nemesia

Annual herb to 30cm, with oval, toothed leaves; bearing compact racemes of bicoloured, snapdragon-like flowers, with small, rounded, white to cream upper petals and a blue to blackish lower lip with a raised, hairy palate at the base, and a short, blunt spur up to 2mm long. The fruits are longer than they are wide. **HABITAT**: Sandy flats and slopes, often after fire, in Namaqualand and the southwestern Cape.

The unusual flowers mimic the gregarious, furry monkey beetles that are their main pollinator. The flowers vary greatly in size, with an exceptionally large-flowered form found around Hopefield.

Aug–Oct   S5 P5 St4 <u>O</u>

S5 P5 St4 <u>O</u>   Aug–Sep

Nemesia strumosa
Pouched nemesia

 Annual herb to 40cm, with narrowly lance-shaped, lightly toothed leaves; bearing crowded, rounded racemes of white, cream, pink, mauve, or sometimes red, flowers that are mottled brown and coarsely hairy in the throat, with a sac-like lower lip and rounded upper petals. The fruits are longer than they are wide. **HABITAT:** Sandy flats, often in Sandveld, along the West Coast.

One of the Cape's most widely cultivated annuals, introduced to England by the Victorian doyenne of Cape cuisine, and celebrated hostess, Hildagonda Duckitt, who collected seeds on the family holiday farm, Bokbaai, near Darling. Plants flower in the wild mainly after fire, and occur in single-coloured populations.

S5 P5 St4 <u>O</u>   Aug–Oct

Diascia capensis
Cape twinspur, Kaapsepensies

Erect or sprawling annual herb to 35cm, with deeply lobed leaves; bearing solitary, greyish-violet flowers 12–23mm in diameter on long, slender stalks, with a dark magenta centre and 2 yellow sacs; the stamens are borne on a yellow swelling and arch upwards. **HABITAT:** Mainly coastal Sandveld in the southwestern Cape.

Some of the perennial twinspurs from the eastern Drakensberg Mountains are popular garden plants. The intricate flowers are pollinated by specialised oil-collecting bees that utilise the floral oils secreted by glands contained in the flower spurs. The Afrikaans vernacular name, *pensie*, is a 17th-century corruption of the English 'pansy'.

Hemimeris racemosa
Sack yellow-face, Geelgesiggies

Annual herb, 3–50cm, with oval, toothed or lobed leaves; bearing clusters of sac-like yellow flowers 7–13mm long, speckled with brown on the 2 upper petals, with an open face, and 2 short spurs 1.5–3mm long. **HABITAT:** Coastal and inland sand and clay soils from Namaqualand to the Eastern Cape. **SIMILAR:** Folded yellow-face, *Hemimeris sabulosa*, has 2 horizontal pockets folded across the face above the stamens.

The complex flowers are pollinated by oil-collecting bees that harvest oils secreted in the two spurs. Some populations have two forms of flowers, one kind with the style flexed upwards under the upper lip and the stamens downwards, and the other form with the reverse arrangement. This is a mechanism to promote cross-pollination.

Jul–Oct   S5 P5 St4 <u>O</u>

Monopsis lutea
Yellow lobelia

Perennial herb with sprawling or trailing stems to 60cm, with narrowly elliptical, toothed leaves, often oriented along the upper side of the stem; bearing bright yellow, 2-lipped, salver-shaped flowers clustered in spikes at the branch tips, twisted so that the upper lip is 3-lobed and the lower is 2-lobed, the tube split down the middle to the base, and the anthers joined to one another. **HABITAT:** Damp flats and lower slopes, often along seeps or streams, in the southwestern and southern Cape.

Yellow lobelia is an ideal rockery plant for coastal gardens and hanging baskets. The orientation of the bright yellow flowers allows them to mimic species of Cape gorse and to share the same leafcutter bees as pollinators. The bees gather pollen directly into special 'baskets' on the underside of their abdomens, from anthers positioned in the bottom lip of the flowers.

Nov–Apr   S5 P5 St5 <u>O</u>

Monopsis debilis
Pansy-lobelia

Loosely sprawling or tufted annual herb, with slender stems to 25cm and narrowly elliptical, toothed leaves; bearing solitary, purple, almost regularly salver-shaped flowers with broad, rounded petals and a darker or black centre, on slender pedicels in the leaf axils, the tube split down the middle to the base, and the anthers joined to one another. **HABITAT:** Damp sandy slopes and flats, often along seepages, in Namaqualand and the southwestern Cape.

A dainty, late-flowering annual with flowers resembling miniature pansies.

S5 P5 St5 O̅   Sep–Dec

Hyobanche sanguinea
Scarlet broomrape, Katnaels, Wolwekos

Root parasite with scale-like leaves lacking green chlorophyll pigment. Bears a dense, rounded spike of densely hairy, crimson red or pink, 2-lipped flowers with a ±cylindrical floral tube enclosing the stamens but with the waxy, white style protruding. **HABITAT:** Sandy slopes and flats from southern Namibia to Swaziland.

A striking plant with the unattractive habit of attaching to the roots of its host plant, often *Eriocephalus* shrubs, and drawing all its nutrients directly from them. The Afrikaans vernacular name *Wolwekos* (hyena-food) is a derisory term for plants not suitable for human consumption. *Katnaels* (cat claws) is an obvious allusion to the white, hook-like styles.

S5 P3 St4 O̲   Aug–Oct

INDEX

GLOSSARY OF TERMS

annual plant that germinates from seed, flowers, produces new seeds, and dies within a single season

anther sac-like structure containing pollen grains, at end of the stamen

awn stiff bristle, often present on the fruits of grasses

axil the upper angle between a stem and an attached leaf or branch

axillary of structures in this position

basal of the base

bract leaf-like organ subtending a flower or inflorescence

calyx collective sepals of a flower, usually leaf-like, protecting the bud

carpel single element or segment of an ovary containing ovules

corm underground storage structure formed from a short, swollen stem

cormous of plants with a corm

corolla the collective petals of a flower, comprising the inner whorl of sterile segments, usually colourful and serving to attract pollinators

ellipsoid rugby ball-shaped

flowerhead head-like inflorescence containing a number of individual small flowers or florets

geophyte perennial plant with underground storage organs, propagates by means of buds below soil surface

half-inferior ovary ovary situated on the floral axis between the insertion of the calyx and corolla

herb applied to a plant lacking woody stems, either short- or long-lived

herbaceous relating to herbs in the botanical (not culinary) sense

inferior ovary ovary situated on the floral axis below the calyx and corolla

keeled bearing a median longitudinal ridge, as the keel of a boat

margin edge

ovary female part of a flower, containing the ovules (eggs)

peduncle stalk of a plant bearing an inflorescence or solitary flower

pedunculate with a peduncle

perennial herbaceous plant that persists for several years, typically having fleshy roots, and leaves clustered at the base of the stem

petal one segment of the inner sterile whorl of a flower, usually colourful; collectively called a corolla

rhizomatous with or like a rhizome

rhizome horizontal plant stem creeping on or underground, usually with buds and scale-like leaves

salver-shaped of flowers with a narrow, cylindrical tube and flat, spreading petals

sepal one segment of the outermost sterile whorl of a flower, usually leaf-like; collectively called a calyx

sessile without a stalk

sheath tubular, protective structure, as in the lower portion of a grass leaf that clasps the stem

short shoot small, highly contracted branch bearing tufts of leaves or flowers

shrub woody plant smaller than a tree, without a single trunk but with several main stems from the base

shrublet small shrub

simple undivided or unbranched

superior ovary ovary situated on the floral axis above the calyx and corolla

spathe large leaf- or petal-like bract enclosing a flower cluster

stamen male part of flower, comprises a sac-like anther, containing pollen grains, borne on the end of a slender stalk or filament

stapeliad one of several, similar species allied to *Stapelia*, a genus of succulent plants with large, star-shaped flowers that smell of carrion

tuber swollen subterranean storage stem or root

whorl a single series of foliar or floral organs radiating from the same point on the floral axis or stem